EXPLORING THE WORLD

STUDENT WORKBOOK

to accompany EXPLORING THE WORLD, 4th Edition

Nona Starr, CTC
Talula Guntner, CTC

The Travel institute

Contents

Introduction

The Workbook has practice worksheets and resource materials, such as Web sites and a selected list of World Heritage Sites, for your use in research and reinforcement. Once you start exploring travel sites on the Internet—and be warned, there are literally millions—you will be able to plan a trip from A to Z.

Newspapers, periodicals, guidebooks, and books about the travel experience fill the need for background information, but you will rarely find such items in the offices of the travel, tourism, and hospitality industries. Almost every resource is online. The time needed to produce and print hard copy has made online access the resource of choice.

Fiction can enhance a travel experience—especially when the reader wants to pass time during travel or settle the mind before bedtime. Many books can easily be taken on a portable device. Each chapter in this Workbook has reading suggestions, some of historical and educational interest, some just for fun.

■ Travel on the Internet

Typically, an Internet site is an extension of an established business, be it an airline, hotel chain, railroad, cruise line, ground transportation provider, tour operator, travel agency, convention and visitors' bureau (CVB), or destination's marketing office. Some are online travel agencies—such as Expedia or Travelocity—designed to serve travelers who want to book trips themselves. Others are owned by groups of airlines or hotels. Still others are set up by local or international tourist bureaus and businesses to sell their regions and products. Always consider the source. Most well-known names in travel are online. But anyone can put up a site. If the name is not familiar, check further. Be aware that the Internet is constantly changing. Sites merge, change, or go out of business without warning. The goals of this Workbook are to help you recognize useful sites and start building your own electronic address book.

Inclusion in this book does not represent endorsement by The Travel Institute, and, while every effort has been made to ensure that online addresses are accurate at the time of printing, Web sites can, and do, change.

Note that when Web site addresses don't end in .com, the end letters show where the site is located. For example, www.railaustralia.com.au, ends with au, the country code for Australia. Other international addresses end in such suffixes as eu and asia.

Each Workbook chapter lists online sites in its Resources section. Just about every travel and tourism organization seems to have one. You can usually find what you want by simply putting in the name or term you are looking for into your search engine and letting it do the work. The way to become an expert is to dig in and practice. Sometimes the best way to learn what's online is simply to keep traveling on it.

■ Attractions

In addition to commercial attractions, such as Walt Disney World, a country's national parks, battlefields, memorials, historic sites, monuments, preserves, seashores, parkways, lakeshores, wild and scenic rivers, trails, and recreation areas attract travelers and spin-off business, especially for the industry's tourism and hospitality segments. In the United States, national park sites are authorized for protection by Congress or by presidential proclamation.

Private organizations, such as National Trusts, also contribute to the preservation of a country's heritage. Some organizations are privately funded; others have limited government protection.

■ UNESCO

The United Nations Educational, Scientific, and Cultural Organization (UNESCO) is an autonomous agency of the United Nations (UN). It has developed the World Heritage List, which names places of importance to tourism either because of their natural heritage or their significant contribution to world culture. Some sites are both natural and cultural.

Some of the world's natural heritage sites are listed in this workbook, but due to space limitations, only a selected list of cultural heritage sites are. UNESCO's Web site, en.unesco.org, displays the most up-to-date sites.

The cultural sites are one of the following types:
- Places of historical interest.
- Significant architectural works.
- Monumental works of sculpture and painting.
- Archaeological sites.

The natural sites are judged for the importance of the following characteristics:
- Significant natural features.
- Habitats of threatened species of outstanding value.
- Outstanding scientific or conservation value or natural beauty.

The World Monuments Fund works on projects with local communities and partners to preserve monuments around the world. Check out the Web site (www.wmf.org) for a current list of their projects.

Destination Geography

■ Resources

Travel companies are always seeking more efficient ways of doing business, particularly relating to technology. Increasing online presence is due in large part to the necessity to be in front of consumers, wherever and whenever they want information that might lead to a product sale.

Accommodations

Some sites list rates and specials; others have pictures and booking information. Although not a reference source for booking accommodations, the American Hotel & Lodging Association is the trade association that represents the interests of the lodging industry. It provides information and support to its membership throughout the world.

American Hotel & Lodging Association
www.ahla.com

Air Travel

As well as being in the trade's Global Distribution Systems (GDSs), airlines host Web sites available to the consumer. Sites with background information that you might like to visit are:

Airlines Reporting Corporation (ARC)
www.arccorp.com

Guide to airports and 3-letter codes
www.quickaid.com

International Air Transport Association (IATA)
www.iatan.org

U.S. Department of Transportation
www.transporation.gov

Cruises

The cruise product continues to grow despite the world's economic and political problems. The product's flexibility is one of its big business advantages. Companies can move their products (ships) to avoid geopolitical hot spots and reroute them to calmer seas, perhaps to ports in Alaska, the Caribbean, or South America. There also has been an increase in "home-porting," which means ships originating from local ports instead of sailings from one port only. This attracts passengers who prefer to drive to the embarkation point instead of having to fly.

Visit Cruise Lines International (CLIA) at www.cruising.org for a list of the major cruise lines.

Cruise line Web sites are listed in the Chapter 6 (Bermuda and the West Indies) resources box. Companies that specialize in one or two destinations only, such as river cruisers, are listed in appropriate chapters.

Currency Questions and Travel Insurance

Information about travel insurance, tipping, and currency conversion is available from:

Currency exchange
www.xe.com

Travel insurance
www.allianztravelinsurance.com
www.travelguard.com

Destination Information

Web sites with destination information are:

Amusement parks
www.iaapa.org

Condé Nast Traveler
www.cntraveler.com

Fodor's Guides
www.fodors.com

Frommer's Guides
www.frommers.com

Lonely Planet Guides
www.lonelyplanet.com

Michelin Guides
www.travelmichelin.com

Moon Travel Handbooks
www.moon.com

National Geographic
www.nationalgeographic.com

National Geographic Traveler
www.nationalgeographic.com/traveler

Special interest travel

www.specialtytravel.com

Travel and Leisure
www.travelandleisure.com

World Travel Guide
www.wtgonline.com

Zagat Guides
www.zagat.com

Destination information is also available from trade associations that represent their member countries. They are:

African Travel Association
www.africa-ata.org

Caribbean Tourism Organization
www.onecaribbean.org

European Travel Commission
www.visiteurope.com

Pacific Asia Travel Association (PATA)
www.pata.org

Events

Travelers often want to link their trips to a special event. For listings, you might try:

The World's Best Festivals
www.fest300.com

Events listed by date, location, type
www.eventsworldwide.com

Guide to North American fairs
www.westernfairs.org

Government Resources

When questions involve safety, health, or customs and documentation regulations, travelers need reliable answers. U.S. government sources for information on health and safety are:

Centers for Disease Control (CDC)
www.cdc.gov/travel

Duty-free allowances
www.cbp.gov/travel/international-visitors/kbyg/customers-duty-info
Federal Aviation Administration
www.faa.gov

U.S. National Parks (alphabetical lists of parks with links to each park and photos)
www.nps.gov

U.S. Passport Office
www.travel.state.gov

World Health Organization (a U.N. agency)
www.who.ch

At www.travel.state.gov/content/passports/en/alertswarnings.html, the State
Department provides:

1. **Consular information sheets** for each foreign country, with information
   about health, crime, and safety considerations. Consular information sheets
   are strictly factual and contain no advice on whether a traveler should or
   should not visit a country.

2. **Public announcements** issued when temporary conditions in a country
   create a security risk that might make someone think twice about going.
   Examples are terrorist threats, political demonstrations, anniversary dates
   of bombings, and events such as earthquakes. Public announcements have
   expiration dates and often are confined to a particular part of a country.

3. **Travel warnings**, the strongest type of release, are issued when the State
   Department recommends avoiding a country.

Maps

The National Geographic Society (nationalgeographic.com) and publisher
Rand McNally (www.randmcnally.com) provide maps online. Other handy
sites include mapquest.com and freetrip.com.

Remember to credit the source if you print out a map (or get permission in
writing if you intend to duplicate a map in any sales literature). Reproducing a
map for anything but personal or educational purposes violates copyright laws.

Road Travel

Web sites make it easy to compare rates and reserve a rental car anywhere in
the world. You might want to begin your search with one of the online travel
agencies. After you have found the best rate, check the car rental company's
own site to see if there are any specials or other savings.

Sports

For information about when and where events are scheduled or where to go to
participate in a favorite sport, contact:

Baseball—major leagues
www.mlb.com

Basketball—National Basketball Association
www.nba.com

Bicycle tours
www.backroads.com

Diving—Association of Diving Instructors (PADI)
www.padi.com

Golf—United States Golf Association (USGA)
www.usga.org

Hiking—American Hiking Society
www.americanhiking.org

Ice hockey—National Hockey League
www.nhl.com

Nature—the Sierra Club
www.sierraclub.org/outings

Ski resorts
www.onthesnow/ski-resort.html

Tennis—U.S. Tennis Association
www.usta.com

Time

Do time zone changes confuse you? The Internet provides help so that vacationers do not call home at 0200 or when everyone has gone to work. Try:

Local time provider
www.worldtimeserver.com

Time zone converter
www.timezoneconverter.com

Tours

Regional and national tour operators are plentiful on the Web. Local tour operators are American Sightseeing International and Grayline Tours. The United States Tour Operators Association (USTOA) and NTA are trade associations representing international and domestic tour operators:

American Sightseeing International
www.sightseeing.com

Grayline Tours
www.grayline.com

United States Tour Operators Association (USTOA)
www.ustoa.com

Weather

You can get 3- to 5-day forecasts for almost any place on earth from:

CNN weather forecasts
www.cnn.com/weather

Forecasts
www.accuweather.com

Hurricane tracking
www.fema.gov

National Weather Service
www.nws.noaa.gov

The Weather Channel
www.weather.com

Using Information

After you have found information, you must judge its usefulness. Factors to consider are:

- **Date.** If you are doing research in rapidly changing areas such as price, schedule, or availability, you need an electronic resource. Be sure to check a site's posting date; some remain unchanged for a long time.

- **Authoritativeness.** Is the information correct? It may be wise to check facts with a second source.

- **Bias.** Does the information have any apparent bias? It would be a rare travel supplier, publication, tour operator, tourist board, hotel, convention and visitors' center, or restaurant site that mentions anything negative.

Worksheet 1.1: Geography

_____   _____
Name   Date

Directions: Answer the questions in the space provided. Answers can be found in your textbook or on a map.

1. What does the word *geography* mean to you? How do you think knowledge of destination geography will benefit you as a travel professional?

   _____

   _____

2. How do cartographers shape our world?

   _____

   _____

3. What do geographers need to know about places on the earth?

   _____

   _____

4. Are lines of longitude and latitude all the same length?

   _____

5. What is a hemisphere? Which one do you live in?

   _____

   _____

6. How does a GPS unit know where you are?

   _____

   _____

7. What does the map's scale tell you?

   _____

8. Why are varying colors on a map sometimes used?

   _____

   _____

9. Which is the largest continent?

   _____

10. What legal implications does the location of a country's continental shelf have for the cruise industry?

_____

_____

11. What is an archipelago? Name three.

_____

_____

12. What is a strait? Name three.

_____

_____

13. Which is the world's largest country?

_____

14. Name the four major oceans?

_____

15. How does elevation affect climate?

_____

16. What is the jet stream? How does it affect an airplane's flight?

_____

17. How do you convert Fahrenheit to Celsius?

_____

18. What is a rain forest? Where are most located?

_____

19. What is a desert? Name three.

_____

_____

20. Name two barriers to travel that create cultural misunderstandings. Why do they do so?

_____

_____

Worksheet 1.2: Answering Questions

_____
Name   Date

Directions: Answer each question in the space provided.

1. You are working at an airline reservations desk. The traveler asks, "How long is my flight from New York City to Los Angeles? From Los Angeles back to New York City? Why is there a difference?" How would you answer?

2. A client asks you, "What guidebook would you recommend for my trip to England?" What would you suggest and why?

Worksheet 1.3: Using Reference Materials

_____

Name   Date

Directions: Using available resources, answer the questions in the space provided. Indicate in your answer what resources you used.

1. What reference source would you consult to determine the health hazards of a trip to the Brazilian rain forest? Did the resource suggest any precautions? If so, what?

2. You need to know the documentation requirements for travel to Australia. Where would you look? What did you find out?

3. What will the weather be like for a cruise around the Horn of South America in March?

4. Ms. Te Kauri wants to know if her health insurance will cover her when she goes bungee-jumping on her New Zealand vacation. What do you tell her?

Worksheet 1.4: Map Review

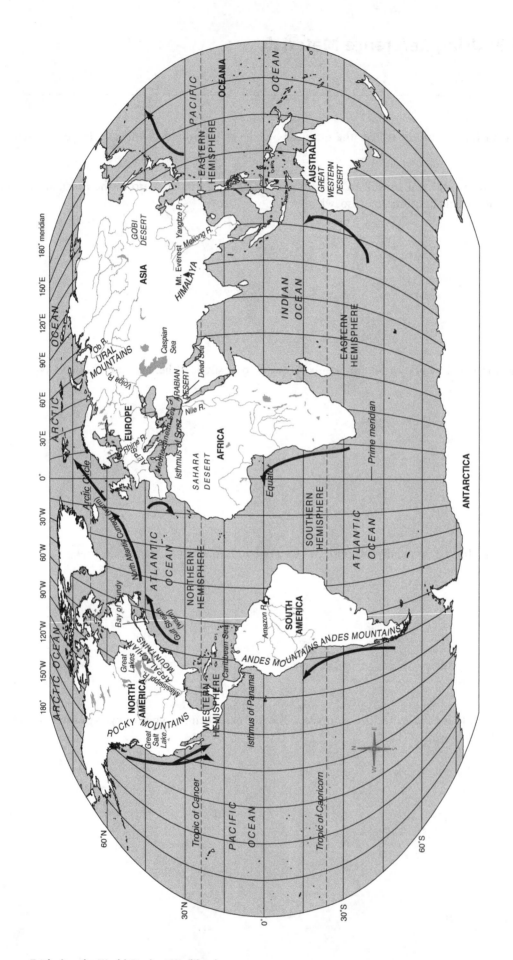

FIGURE 1.1 Earth

▲ National park or other site
1 inch = 2,316 miles (3,726 km)

Worksheet 1.4: Map Review

Name _____ Date _____

Directions: Using the map on the preceding page, answer the following questions.

1. What is the map's scale?

   _____

2. What feature on the map indicates its directional orientation?

   _____

3. Most people are familiar with the equator, but where would you be if you were at a latitude of 23.5° north of the equator, the farthest point at which the sun can be seen directly overhead at noon?

   _____

4. If you were to fly due west from Ireland to North America, you would reach the lower region of Hudson Bay in Canada, which is on the same latitude as Ireland. Why, then, is Ireland's climate so mild?

   _____

   _____

5. Name the mountain range that serves as a boundary between Europe and northern Asia.

   _____

6. The Appalachian Mountain Range is the principal mountain landform on North America's East Coast. Which mountain range is the West Coast's principal landform?

   _____

7. Which continent is the only one with land in all four hemispheres?

   _____

8. Which is the only continent other than Antarctica that does not extend into the tropics?

   _____

9. How many degrees of longitude would you cross to travel halfway around the world?

   _____

10. The equator is to latitude as which of the following is to longitude?
    A. Tropic of Cancer
    B. Tropic of Capricorn
    C. International date line
    D. Prime meridian

Worksheet 1.5: Looking Back: A Chapter Quiz

Name _____ Date _____

Directions: Answer the questions in the space provided.

1. What is the shortest, most direct route between any two points on the surface of the earth?

   _____

2. Convert the following times from AM and PM to the 24-hour clock.

   A. 1:20 PM _____   C. 10:30 AM _____

   B. 8:08 AM _____   D. 11:59 PM _____

3. Convert the following times from the 24-hour clock to AM and PM.

   A. 1306 _____   C. 0800 _____

   B. 1845 _____   D. 2347 _____

4. You need to contact a hotel in Vienna, Austria (GMT + 2). What time should you make a phone call to be assured that the hotel's reservations office will receive your call about 10:00 AM Vienna time?

   _____

5. If it rains on your golf game in Hawaii, is the cause climate or weather?

   _____

6. Why would a destination near the equator require a visitor to bring a heavy sweater?

   _____

   _____

7. Match each term with the correct definition. Write the definition's letter in the blank at the left of each term.

   _____ tropics   A. Cold or warm rivers of sea water.

   _____ rain shadow   B. Latitudes between the Tropic of Cancer and the Tropic of
                                       Capricorn.

   _____ trade winds   C. The dry area on the leeward side of a mountain.

   _____ westerlies   D. Constant winds that blow from the northeast toward the equator in
                                       the Northern Hemisphere and from the southeast toward the equator
                                       in the Southern Hemisphere.

   _____ ocean currents   E. Currents of air high above the earth, blowing from the southwest in
                                       the Northern Hemisphere and from the northwest in the Southern
                                       Hemisphere.

The Eastern United States

■ Resources

Today the Internet provides just about anything anyone wants to know. The ease of updating makes the online information far more current than any paper resource. Even magazines are online. For trips to the southern states, the regional magazine *Southern Living* (www.southernliving.com) offers destination news, and *Yankee Magazine* (www.yankeemagazine.com) aids travelers to New England. *Midwest Living* and *Sunset* are sources for their regions. See their Web listings in Chapters 3 and 4.

American Cruise Lines
www.americancruiselines.com

U.S. rail travel
www.amtrak.com

Alabama
www.alabama.travel

Mobile
www.mobile.org

Connecticut
www.tourism.state.ct

Foxwoods
www.foxwoods.com

Mystic Seaport
www.visitmystic.com

Delaware
www.visitdelaware.com

Brandywine Valley
www.visitwilmingtonde.com

District of Columbia
www.washington.org

Ford's Theatre
www.fordstheatre.org

Kennedy Center
www.kennedy-center.org

Mount Vernon
www.mountvernon.org

Smithsonian Museums
www.si.edu

White House
www.nps.gov/whho

Florida
www.flausa.com

Amelia Island
www.ameliaisland.com

Everglades
www.nps.gov/ever

Florida Keys
www.fla-keys.com

Fort Lauderdale
www.sunny.org

Fort Myers/Sanibel
www.portmyers-sanibel.com

Kennedy Space Center
www.kennedyspacecenter.com

Marco Island
www.marcoislandchamber.org

Miami
www.miamiandbeaches.com

Orlando
www.visitorlando.com

Palm Beach
www.palmbeachfl.com

Pensacola
www.visitpensacola.com

Sea World/Busch Gardens
seaworld.org

Universal Studios Florida
www.universalstudios.com

Villa Vizcaya
www.vizcayamuseum.com

Walt Disney World
www.disneyworld.com

Georgia
www.exploregeorgia.org

Atlanta
www.atlanta.com

Golden Isles
www.golendisles.com

Savannah
www.visitsavannah.com

Kentucky
www.kentuckytourism.com

Lexington
www.visitlex.com

Louisiana
www.louisianatravel.com

Lafayette
www.lafayettetravel.com

New Orleans
www.neworleanscvb.com

Maine
www.visitmaine.com

Acadia National Park
www.nps.gov/acad

Kennebunk
www.visitthekennebunks.com

Sunday River
www.sundayriver.com

Windjammers
www.sailmainecoast.com

Maryland
www.maryland.com

Annapolis
www.visit-annapolis.org

Baltimore
www.baltimore.org

Chesapeake Bay cruises
www.cruisesonthebay.com

Massachusetts
www.massvacation.com

Berkshires
www.berkshires.org

Boston
www.bostonusa.com

Boston North
www.northofboston.org

Cape Cod
www.capecodchamber.org

Freedom Trail
www.thefreedomtrail.org

Martha's Vineyard
www.mvy.com

Mississippi
www.visitmississippi.org

Biloxi-Gulfport
www.gulfcoast.org

Natchez
www.visitnatchez.org

Natchez Trace
www.scenictrace.com

Tupelo
www.tupelo.net

Vicksburg
www.visitvicksburg.com

New Hampshire
www.visitnh.com

Attitash
www.attitash.com

Bretton Woods
www.brettonwoods.com

Cog Railway
www.thecog.com

Waterville Valley
www.waterville.com

New Jersey
www.visitnj.org

Atlantic City
www.atlanticcitynj.com

Cape May
www.capemaychamber.com

New York
www.iloveny.com

Catskill Region
www.visitthecatskills.com

Empire State Building
www.esbnyc.com

Finger Lakes
www.fingerlakes.org

Long Island
www.discoverlongisland.com

New York City
www.nycvisit.com

Niagara Falls
www.niagarafallstourism.com

Playbill (NYC theaters)
www.playbill.com

Statue of Liberty
www.nps.gov/stli

Theater tickets
www.broadway.com

Thousand Islands
www.visit1000islands.com

North Carolina
www.visitnc.com

Asheville
www.exploreasheville.org

Biltmore Estate
www.biltmore.com

Outer Banks
www.outerbanks.org

Pennsylvania
www.visitpa.com

Bucks County
www.experiencebuckscounty.com

Gettysburg
www.destinationgettysburg.com

Lancaster County
www.padutchcountry.com

National Constitution Center
www.constitutioncenter.org

Philadelphia
www.visitphila.com

Pittsburgh
www.visitpittsburgh.com

Valley Forge
www.valleyforge.org

Rhode Island
www.visitrhodeisland.com

Block Island
www.blockislandchamber.com

Newport
www.discovernewport.org

Newport mansions
www.newportmansions.org

Providence
www.goprovidence.com

South Carolina
www.travelsc.com

Charleston
www.charlestoncvb.com

Hilton Head
www.hiltonheadisland.org

Low Country
www.southcarolinalowcountry.com

Myrtle Beach
www.myrtlebeach.com

Sea Pines
www.seapines.com

Tennessee
www.tnvacation.com

Chattanooga
www.chattanoogafun.com

Dollywood
www.dollywood.com

Graceland
www.graceland.com

Grand Ole Opry
www.opry.com

Memphis
www.memphistravel.com

Nashville
www.visitmusiccity.com

Vermont
www.travelvermont.com

Killington
www.killington.com

Lake Champlain CVB
www.vermont.org

Mount Snow
www.mountsnow.com

Smugglers' Notch
www.smuggs.com

Stowe
www.stowe.com

Stratton Mountain
www.stratton.com

Sugarbush
www.sugarbush.com

Virginia
www.virginia.org

Blue Ridge Parkway
www.nps.gov/blri

Northern Virginia
www.fxva.com

Virginia Beach
www.vbfun.com

Williamsburg
www.colonialwilliamsburg.com

Wolf Trap Park
www.wolftrap.org

West Virginia
www.gotowv.com

Charleston
www.charlestonwv.com

state parks
www.wvstateparks.com

■ UNESCO World Heritage Sites

For the Eastern United States, the UNESCO World Heritage List includes the following:

Cultural Heritage

- Independence Hall, Pennsylvania
- Monticello and the University of Virginia, Virginia
- Statue of Liberty, New York

Natural Heritage

- *Everglades National Park, Florida
- Great Smoky Mountains National Park, Tennessee and North Carolina
- Mammoth Cave National Park, Kentucky

■ Reading Suggestions: The Eastern United States

- Louisa May Alcott (1832–1888): Her novels *Little Women* and *Little Men*, written to contribute to the family income, have become classics; her childhood home in Concord, Massachusetts, is a tourist attraction.

- John Berendt: *Midnight in the Garden of Good and Evil* (1994) covers society life and murder in Savannah, Georgia.

- Bruce Catton: *A Stillness at Appomattox* (1953) is the Pulitzer Prize–winning final volume of his *Army of the Potomac* trilogy.

- Frank Conroy: *Time and Tides: A Walk through Nantucket* (2004) is a story about the island's evolution from an isolated whalers' station to one of the most prestigious vacation addresses on the East Coast.

- John Jakes: *North and South* (1982) is a Civil War potboiler.

- Frances Parkinson Keys: *Dinner at Antoine's* (1948) is a murder mystery set in New Orleans a few weeks before Mardi Gras.

- Henry Wadsworth Longfellow (1807–1882): His narrative poems *Evangeline, Hiawatha, The Courtship of Miles Standish, Paul Revere's Ride*, and *Tales of a Wayside Inn* did a great deal to develop audiences for poetry in America.

- James Michener: *Chesapeake* (1978) is a history of the bay.

- Margaret Mitchell: *Gone with the Wind* (1936) is a Civil War novel and the winner of a Pulitzer Prize, with more than 30 million copies in 32 languages.

- Michael Sharra: *The Killer Angels* (1975) is the Civil War's Battle of Gettysburg. Work of Jeff Sharra continues his father's epics.

- Les Standiford: *Last Train to Paradise* (2002) is the story of Henry Flagler's dream to build a railroad across the sea to Key West.

- Smithsonian series: *The Smithsonian Guides to Historic America* (many revisions) is an easy-to-read series with many pictures, good reference material.

Worksheet 2.1: Geography

Name _____ Date _____

Directions: Answer the questions in the space provided. Answers can be found by looking either in your textbook or at a map.

1. Name three barrier islands off the East Coast of the United States.

   _____

   _____

2. What does it mean when geographers say a place is part of an area called the Piedmont? Give an example of a state where the Piedmont is most obvious.

   _____

   _____

3. Why did the fall line limit explorers' ship travel?

   _____

   _____

4. What mountain system stretches north–south from Canada to Alabama? Name at least three of its ranges.

   _____

   _____

5. What is a delta?

   _____

   _____

6. Why was the Erie Canal so important in its time?

   _____

   _____

7. Name New York City's five boroughs.

   _____

   _____

8. What resort bills itself as the "Nation's Summer Capital" and why?

_____

_____

9. Why do you think graves are above ground in Louisiana?

_____

_____

10. Describe some of the geological features of the Florida peninsula.

_____

_____

Worksheet 2.2: Itinerary Planning

Name   Date

The travelers, a couple in their twenties, are spending a long weekend (3 days) in New Orleans. You are working for the city's tourist board, and they come to you for information about what to see and do in the city. What questions do you ask the couple before you make recommendations? It is not enough to ask where they have been in the past or what hotels they have used. Good customer relationship management must include gathering as much knowledge as possible about what makes potential customers tick. Outline their answers before you make suggestions.

Worksheet 2.3: Answering Questions

_____
Name   Date

Directions: How would you respond to travelers who ask the following questions?

1. "Aren't New York City theater tickets too expensive?"

2. "You recommend using public transportation in the big cities. Aren't subway systems dangerous?"

3. A traveler who lives in Maryland says: "My daughter, who lives in central Florida, and I would like to meet midway in late March. Do you have any suggestions for a destination where we could shop, relax, and do a little sightseeing? Neither of us plays golf, and I no longer enjoy sitting on the beach for hours."

4. "What do you do at a theme park if it rains or gets hot?"

Worksheet 2.4: Map Review

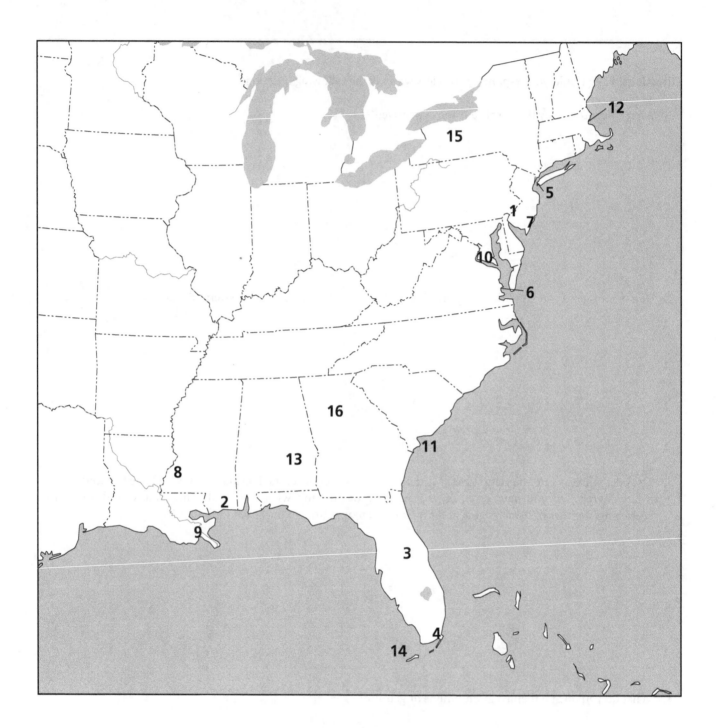

Worksheet 2.4: Map Review

_____
Name   Date

Directions: In the following exercises, give the three-letter airport code of the destination or of the nearest airport city. Optional: Use industry or online resources to find the airport code of the destination or the nearest airport.

1. Match the New England or New York destination with its number on the map.

   Map Number   **Airport Code**

   _____   Broadway   _____

   _____   Faneuil Hall   _____

   _____   Finger Lakes   _____

2. Match the Mid-Atlantic destination with its number on the map.

   _____   Atlantic City   _____

   _____   Liberty Bell   _____

   _____   Mount Vernon   _____

3. Match the southern destination with its number on the map.

   _____   Atlanta   _____

   _____   Hilton Head   _____

   _____   Williamsburg   _____

4. Match the Florida destination with its number on the map.

   _____   Key West   _____

   _____   South Beach   _____

   _____   Walt Disney World   _____

5. Match the Gulf Coast destination with its number on the map.

   _____   Bourbon Street   _____

   _____   Gulfport   _____

   _____   Memorial Baptist Church _____

   _____   Natchez   _____

Worksheet 2.5: Using Reference Materials

Name   Date

Directions: Using available resources, answer the questions in the space provided. Indicate in your answer what resources you used.

1. You are organizing a tour to New York City. The group leader tells you that participants would like to see a Broadway show. Choose a current hit show. What is the approximate cost for an orchestra seat? Are any group rates available?

2. What budget hotel accommodations are available in New York City? List three possibilities and their rates.

3. Does Walt Disney World have any package plans that include admission tickets and on-site hotels? Provide details for one.

Worksheet 2.6: Looking Back: A Chapter Quiz

Name _____ Date _____

Directions: Answer the questions in the space provided, or circle the correct answer.

1. Which city or area would have special appeal to its niche travelers?

   _____ History explorers   A. Orlando, Florida

   _____ Gourmets   B. Hudson River Valley, New York

   _____ Wine tasters   C. Boston, Massachusetts

   _____ Harness-racing fans   D. Camden, Maine

   _____ Windjammer cruisers   E. Newport, Rhode Island

   _____ Theme park lovers   F. Finger Lakes area, New York

   _____ Mansion admirers   G. Saratoga, New York

2. Name a mountain range in each state.

   New Hampshire   _____

   Vermont   _____

   New York   _____

   North Carolina _____

   Virginia   _____

3. How would you characterize the climate of South Florida?

   _____

4. When is the official hurricane season for the East Coast?

   _____

5. The travelers live in New York City and want to visit a resort and do some gambling. Name two destinations within a few hours' drive.

   _____

   _____

6. Name five home port cities that cruise ships are using along the East Coast.

_____

_____

_____

7. Amber and Maurice are headed to New York City on their honeymoon. They have heard that if they get up early and go to the NBC-TV studios, they stand a chance of getting to wave to the folks back home and be on the *Today* show. Where in the city should they go?

_____

_____

8. Which New Orleans neighborhood is home to Bourbon Street?
   A. Lee Circle
   B. Warehouse Arts District
   C. French Quarter
   D. Carollton

9. Some travelers would like to plan a trip in the eastern United States to try different types of food. Where would you suggest they go?

_____

_____

_____

10. What is the "Run for the Roses," and where does it take place?

_____

_____

11. Some cities roll up their sidewalks at night; others roll them out. The travelers would like a lot of nighttime activity. Where do you think they should go? Give three choices.

_____

_____

12. What are the attractions of Mississippi's Gulf Coast?

_____

_____

The Midwest

■ Resources

Great Lakes
www.glna.org

Lake cruising
www.greatlakescruising.com

Midwest Living (magazine)
www.midwestliving.com

Rail travel
www.amtrak.com

Arkansas
www.arkansas.com

Hot Springs
www.hotsprings.org

Little Rock
www.littlerock.com

Illinois
www.enjoyillinois.com

Cahokia Mounds
www.cahokiamounds.com

Chicago
www.choosechicago.com

Springfield
www.visitspringfieldillinois.com

Willis Tower
www.willistower.com

Indiana
www.visitindianatourism.com

Bloomington
www.visitbloomington.com

Indianapolis
www.visitindy.com

Iowa
www.traveliowa.com

Des Moines
www.catchdesmoines.com

Kansas
www.travelks.com

Michigan
www.michigan.org

Detroit
www.visitdetroit.com

Minnesota
www.exploreminnesota.com

Mall of America
www.mallofamerica.com

Minneapolis
www.minneapolis.org

St. Paul
www.visitstpaul.com

Missouri
www.visitmo.com

Branson
www.explorebranson.com

Gateway Arch
www.gatewayarch.com

Hannibal
www.visithannibal.com

St. Louis
www.explorestlouis.com

Nebraska
www.visitnebraska.org

Henry Doorly Zoo
www.omahazoo.com

Lincoln
www.lincoln.org

Omaha
www.visitomaha.com

North Dakota
www.ndtourism.com

Ohio
www.discoverohio.com

Cincinnati
www.cincyusa.com

Cleveland
www.thisiscleveland.com

Columbus
www.columbuscvb.org

Rock and Roll Hall of Fame
rockhall.com

Oklahoma
www.oktourism.com

Oklahoma City
www.visitokc.com

Tulsa
www.visittulsa.com

South Dakota
www.travelsouthdakota.com

Rapid City
www.visitrapidcity.com

Sioux Falls
www.visitsiouxfalls.com

Texas
www.traveltexas.com

Austin
www.austintexas.org

Bandera
www.banderacowboycapital.com

Corpus Christi
www.visitcorpuschristitx.org

Dallas
www.visitdallas.com

El Paso
www.visitelpaso.com

Fort Worth
www.fortworth.com

Galveston Island
www.galveston.com

Houston
www.visithoustontexas.com

San Antonio
www.visitsanantonio.com

Wisconsin
www.travelwisconsin.com

Madison
www.visitmadison.com

Milwaukee
www.visitmilwaukee.org

■ UNESCO World Heritage Sites

For the Midwest, the UNESCO World Heritage List includes the following:

Cultural Heritage

■ Cahokia Mounds State Historic Site, Illinois

Natural Heritage

None

■ Reading Suggestions: The Midwest

■ Willa Cather: *O Pioneers!* (1913) and *My Antonia* (1918) are stories she had heard as a child from Swedish immigrants in Nebraska.

■ Edna Ferber: *Giant* (1952) is a story of Texas oil, and *Cimarron* (1930), a story of the land rush of 1889 in Oklahoma.

■ William Least Heat-Moon: *Blue Highways* (1982) is about a journey on America's back roads.

■ James Michener: *Texas* (1985) offers more about the state.

■ Upton Sinclair: *The Jungle* (1906) is a novel about Chicago, immigrants, and the meatpacking industry.

■ John Steinbeck: *The Grapes of Wrath* (1939) tells of family members forced out of their home in the Oklahoma Dust Bowl and their migration to California.

■ Laura Ingalls Wilder: *Little House on the Prairie* (1930s) series contain books about pioneer life and was the basis of a popular TV series from 1974 to 1983.

Worksheet 3.1: Geography

Name _____   Date _____

Directions: Answer the questions in the space provided.

1. What will the weather in Chicago be like in May?

   _____

2. What is Columbus, Indiana, known for?

   _____

   _____

3. Which Great Lake is the only one entirely in the United States?

   _____

4. Texas has water borders on two of its sides. Name the bodies of water.

   _____

   _____

5. Describe the physical characteristics of the land that stretches from the Appalachian Highlands to the Rocky Mountains.

   _____

   _____

   _____

   _____

6. What are tornadoes? Where is Tornado Alley?

   _____

   _____

   _____

Worksheet 3.2: Itinerary Planning

_____
Name   Date

You are working for one of the auto clubs. Outline a 7-day driving trip through Texas for a family of four. They plan to go during the children's (ages 10 and 13) spring vacation. They will fly to San Antonio from their home in Chicago and then rent a car at the airport.

Worksheet 3.3: Answering Questions

Name   Date

Directions: How would you respond to travelers who ask the following questions?

1. "I'm a very picky eater. What if I don't like the food on the tour?"

2. "We are taking our children (ages 12 and 14) along on this driving trip to the Badlands. What can they do in addition to seeing the scenery?"

Worksheet 3.4: Map Review

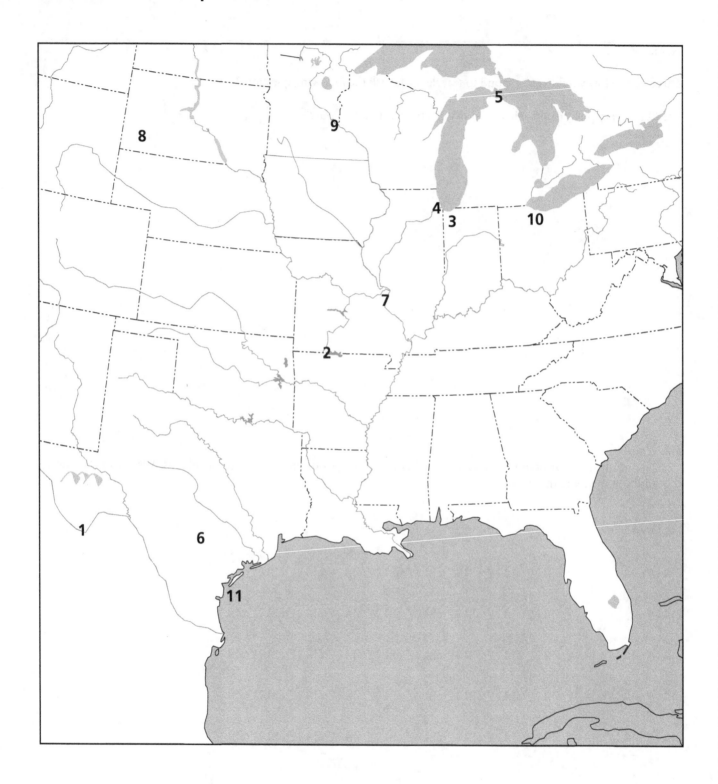

Worksheet 3.4: Map Review

_____
Name   Date

Directions: Match the destination with its number on the map. Optional: Use industry or online resources to find the airport code of the nearest destination or the nearest airport.

Map Number   **Airport Code**

_____   Alamo   _____

_____   Big Bend National Park   _____

_____   Branson   _____

_____   Gateway Arch   _____

_____   Guthrie Theater   _____

_____   Indiana Dunes National Lakeshore   _____

_____   Mackinac Island   _____

_____   Mount Rushmore   _____

_____   Padre Island   _____

_____   Rock and Roll Hall of Fame   _____

_____   The Loop   _____

Worksheet 3.5: Using Reference Materials

Name   Date

Directions: Using available resources, answer the questions in the space provided. Indicate in your answer what resources you used.

1. What is playing in the theaters of Branson?

2. What are some of the activities and promotions presently drawing visitors to Chicago?

3. What is the weather like in Corpus Christi today?

4. How far is the Dallas/Fort Worth Airport from downtown Dallas? Approximately what is the cab or shuttle bus fare?

Worksheet 3.6: Looking Back: A Chapter Quiz

Name _____   Date _____

Matching

Directions: Match the states with their attractions or cities.

Missouri   Arkansas   Kansas   South Dakota   Oklahoma

Iowa   Texas   Nebraska   North Dakota

1. Lewis and Clark passed through it while exploring the West. Its largest city is Fargo.

   _____

2. It is called the *Gateway to the West*, with Mark Twain country and Branson.

   _____

3. It is the largest of the lower forty-eight. The Rio Grande is part of its southern border with Mexico.

   _____

4. Fertile plains attracted members of a German religious sect.

   _____

5. Scotts Bluff marked the way west, and Buffalo Bill was a prominent citizen of this state.

   _____

6. It is home to the Black Hills and the Badlands.

   _____

7. The Santa Fe and Chisholm Trails pass through. The Eisenhower Library is in Abilene.

   _____

8. The Ouachitas are its mountains, and Hot Springs is the place to take a relaxing bath.

   _____

9. It is the home of many Native American tribes and the National Cowboy & Western Heritage Museum.

   _____

True or False

Directions: Circle either True or False.

True   False   1. Lake Erie is the only one of the Great Lakes entirely in the United States.

True   False   2. Tornado Alley includes the states of Texas, Oklahoma, Kansas, Nebraska, and Iowa.

True   False   3. The Ozark-Ouachita Highlands rise in southern Missouri, northwestern Arkansas, and eastern Oklahoma.

True   False   4. Auto racing fans head to Great Bend, Indiana, for the annual 500 race.

True   False   5. Mackinac Island is a summer resort between Lakes Huron and Michigan.

True   False   6. The northern part of Wisconsin is a barren region with few trees.

True   False   7. Frank Lloyd Wright was a famous poet who wrote about Chicago.

True   False   8. Some of Chicago's attractions are the Field Museum of Natural History and Robie House.

True   False   9. The Mall of America is located near the Minneapolis Airport.

True   False   10. Gateway Arch in St. Louis, Missouri, is a monument to westward expansion.

True   False   11. The National Cowboy & Western Heritage Museum is in Oklahoma City.

True   False   12. Nebraska is home to Boot Hill Cemetery and the Eisenhower Library.

The Western States, Alaska, and Hawaii

■ Resources

Dude Ranch Association
www.duderanch.org

Rail travel
www.amtrak.com

Sunset magazine
www.sunset.com

Alaska

www.travelalaska.com

Alaska Highway
www.themilepost.com

Alaska Railroad
www.alaskarailroad.com

Anchorage
www.anchorage.net

Fairbanks
www.explorefairbanks.com

Iditarod
www.iditarod.com

Juneau
www.traveljuneau.com

White Pass & Yukon Route Railroad
www.wpyr.com

Arizona

www.arizonaguide.com

Flagstaff
www.flagstaffarizona.org

Grand Canyon
www.nps.gov/grca

Phoenix
www.visitphoenix.com

Scottsdale
www.experiencescottsdale.com

Tucson
www.visittucson.org

California

www.visitcalifornia.com

Alcatraz
www.nps.gov/alcatraz

Death Valley
www.nps.gov/deva

Disneyland
www.disneyland. go.com

Golden Gate Bridge
www.goldengatebridge.org

Hearst Castle
www.hearstcastle.org

Los Angeles
www.discoverlosangeles.com

Monterey
www.seemonterey.com

Napa Valley
www.napavalley.com

Palm Springs
www.visitpalmsprings.com

San Diego
www.sandiego.org

San Diego Zoo
www.sandiegozoo.org

San Francisco
www.sanfrancisco.travel

Universal Studios
www.universalstudios.com

Yosemite
www.nps.gov/yose

Colorado

www.colorado.com

Aspen
www.aspenchamber.org

Breckenridge
www.breckenridge.com

Colorado Ski Country
www.coloradoski.com

Colorado Springs
www.visitcos.com

Denver
www.denver.org

Estes Park
www.visitestespark.com

Gunnison-Crested Butte
www.gunnisoncrestedbutte.com

Steamboat
www.steamboatchamber.com

Vail
www.snow.com

Hawaii

www.gohawaii.com

Bishop Museum
www.bishopmuseum.org

Dole Plantation
www.dole-plantation.com

Hawaii (the island)
www.gohawaii.com/en/big-island

Iolani Palace
www.iolanipalace.org

Kauai
www.gohawaii.com/en/kauai

Lanai
www.gohawaii.com/en/lanai

Maui
www.gohawaii.com/en/maui

Molokai
www.gohawaii.com/en/molokai

Oahu
www.gohawaii.com/en/oahu

Idaho

www.visitidaho.org

Boise
www.boise.org

Montana

www.visitmt.com

Nevada

www.travelnevada.com

Carson City
www.visitcarsoncity.com

Hoover Dam
www.usbr.gov/lc/hooverdam

Las Vegas
www.lasvegas.com

Las Vegas monorail
www.lvmonorail.com

Reno-Sparks
www.visitrenotahoe.com

Tahoe
www.visitinglaketahoe.com

New Mexico

www.newmexico.org

Albuquerque
www.visitalbuquerque.org

Carlsbad
www.nps.gov/cave

Chaco National Park
www.nps.gov/chcu

Cumbres & Toltec Rail
www.cumbrestoltec.com

Indian Arts and Culture
www.miaclab.org

Indian Pueblo Culture Center
www.indianpueblo.org

Santa Fe
www.santafe.org

Taos
www.taoschamber.com

Oregon

www.traveloregon.com

Columbia River Gorge
www.columbiarivergorge.info

Portland
www.travelportland.com

Utah

www.utah.com

Canyonlands
www.discovermoab.com

Dinosaurland
www.dinoland.com

Salt Lake City
www.visitsaltlake.com

Washington

www.experiencewa.com

Seattle
www.visitseattle.org

Space Needle
www.spaceneedle.com

Spokane
www.visitspokane.com

Wyoming

www.wyomingtourism.org

Cheyenne
www.cheyenne.org

Jackson Hole
www.jacksonholewy.com

Yellowstone
www.nps.gov.yell

■ UNESCO World Heritage Sites

For the western states, Alaska, and Hawaii, the UNESCO World Heritage List includes the following:

Cultural Heritage

- Chaco Culture National Historical Park, New Mexico
- Mesa Verde National Park, Colorado
- Pueblo de Taos, New Mexico

Natural Heritage

- Carlsbad Caverns National Park, New Mexico
- Grand Canyon National Park, Arizona
- Hawaii Volcanoes National Park, Hawaii
- Olympic National Park, Washington
- Redwood National Park, California
- Waterton-Glacier International Peace Park, Montana
- *Yellowstone National Park, Wyoming
- Yosemite National Park, California

■ Reading Suggestions: The Western States, Alaska, and Hawaii

- Stephen E. Ambrose: *Undaunted Courage* (2004) is a historian's account of the Lewis and Clark mission.
- Ben Mezrich: *Bringing Down the House: The Inside Story of Six MIT Students Who Took Vegas for Millions* (2004) is about winning, winning, winning.
- James Michener: *Centennial* (1974), *Hawaii* (1957), and *Alaska* (1988) are sweeping narratives mixing fact and fiction.
- John Steinbeck: *Cannery Row* (1945) and its sequel, *Sweet Thursday* (1954), follow the adventures of workers in a California cannery.

Worksheet 4.1: Geography

Name _____ Date _____

Directions: Answer the questions in the space provided.

1. Which city is farther west: Los Angeles, California, or Reno, Nevada?

    _____

2. What is a continental divide?

    _____

3. What are the highest and lowest elevations in the United States? Where are they?

    _____

    _____

4. What features dominate Alaska's landscape?

    _____

5. What forces of nature formed the Grand Canyon? In what U.S. state is it located?

    _____

    _____

6. Which mountain ranges run north–south through western Washington and Oregon and most of California?

    _____

7. What is a fault? What is the significance of the one called San Andreas?

    _____

    _____

    _____

8. In what U.S. state does it rain the most?

    _____

Worksheet 4.2: Itinerary Planning

Name _____   Date _____

You are working for the California Tourist Board. Outline a trip through the state for a family of four departing from Kansas City. The children's ages are 14 and 12. The family enjoys the outdoors but wants some tips for city sightseeing, especially in San Francisco.

Worksheet 4.3: Answering Questions

Name   Date

Directions: How would you respond to travelers in the following situations?

1. You are employed by a tour operator specializing in Las Vegas trips. A phone customer says: "I know there are bargains to be had at hotels and restaurants in Las Vegas and wonder what tips you could offer to help us find the good deals. Is there a value season?"

2. You are working for New Mexico's tourist board. The traveler says: "I plan to take my grandson to New Mexico as a graduation present. We both are interested in Native American culture. Any recommendations?"

3. "My husband and I are going to Oahu for the first time and wonder if there any must-sees and must-dos beyond the usual tourist haunts?"

Worksheet 4.4: Map Review

Worksheet 4.4: Map Review

Name   Date

Directions: Answer the questions in the space provided. Match the destination with its number on the map. Optional: Use industry or online resources to find the airport code of the nearest destination or the nearest airport.

1. **Map Number**   **Airport Code**

   _____   Anchorage   _____

   _____   Barrow   _____

   _____   Denali   _____

   _____   Fairbanks   _____

   _____   Juneau   _____

   _____   Nome   _____

   _____   Skagway   _____

2. Which points are above the Arctic Circle?

   _____

   _____

3. Which cities are on the Alaska Panhandle?

   _____

   _____

4. Match the island with its number on the map of Hawaii. Give the three-letter code of the island's airport.

   Map Number   **Airport Code**

   _____   Hawaii   _____

   _____   Kauai   _____

   _____   Lanai   _____

   _____   Maui   _____

   _____   Molokai   _____

   _____   Oahu   _____

Worksheet 4.5: Using Reference Materials

Name   Date

Directions: Answer the questions in the space provided. Indicate in your answer what resources you used.

1. How are the ski conditions in Aspen today?

2. What well-known stars are appearing in Las Vegas this week?

3. What documentation is required from a U.S. citizen who wants to cross the Mexican border at San Diego and spend the day in Tijuana?

4. Name three five-star resorts in or near Phoenix, Arizona.

5. What is the weather like today in Denali?

Worksheet 4.6: Looking Back: A Chapter Quiz

Name _____ Date _____

Matching

1. **Directions:** Match the city with its sights.

Albuquerque	Denver	Las Vegas	Los Angeles	Phoenix
Salt Lake City	San Diego	San Francisco	Santa Fe	

A. Ghirardelli Square, Lombard Street, and Fisherman's Wharf _____

B. Taliesin West and Camelback Mountain _____

C. The Strip and Hoover Dam _____

D. Balboa Park and Cabrillo Monument _____

E. Olvera Street and the Walt Disney Concert Hall _____

F. Art, opera, adobe homes, and pueblos _____

G. Molly Brown and LoDo _____

H. Largest city in New Mexico and famous balloon festival _____

I. Temple Square and the Tabernacle _____

2. **Directions:** Match the state with its description and attractions. Some states are used more than once.

Idaho	Montana	Oregon	Washington

A. It has the Going-to-the-Sun Highway and is where Custer made his last stand. _____

B. It is timber country with the Columbia River Gorge. _____

C. The Olympic Peninsula and Mount Saint Helens are part of its natural beauty. _____

D. The state's cities include Billings, Helena, and Butte. _____

E. Attractions include the Selway-Bitterroot Wilderness and the Frank Church River of No Return Wilderness Area. _____

F. The state's largest city celebrates the Rose Festival in June. _____

3. **Directions:** Match the Hawaiian island with its description.

Hawaii   Kauai   Lanai   Maui   Molokai   Oahu

A. Once a pineapple ranch, it is now a low-key resort with good golf courses.

_____

B. Once a leper colony, it is now welcoming and peaceful, with unspoiled beauty.

_____

C. The largest island, it is known for its active volcanoes.

_____

D. The busiest island, it is home to the Polynesian Cultural Center.

_____

E. It is the lushest island, with canyons and cliffs.

_____

F. A paved road leads to an extinct volcano where you can enjoy viewing the sunrise.

_____

Multiple Choice

Directions: Circle the answer to the statement or question.

1. The tallest mountain on the North American continent is
   A. Mount Hood.
   B. Denali.
   C. Mount Rainier.
   D. Mount Whitney.

2. Which state is mainly owned by the federal government?
   A. California
   B. Hawaii
   C. Washington
   D. Alaska

3. What city began as a Mormon mission?
   A. Los Angeles
   B. Seattle
   C. Las Vegas
   D. San Diego

4. It never really gets dark in northern Alaska during
   A. June.
   B. September.
   C. December.
   D. March.

5. The Alaska Marine Highway is
   A. a system of ferry boats along the coast.
   B. a highway along the coast of the Panhandle.
   C. a cruise ship route through the Inland Passage.
   D. a system of floatplanes that service the state.

Worksheet 4.6: Looking Back: A Chapter Quiz (continued)

Name   Date

6. Which of the following Alaskan destinations cannot be reached by car?
   A. Fairbanks
   B. Denali
   C. Glacier Bay
   D. Anchorage

7. On which Hawaiian island does it rain the most?
   A. Oahu
   B. Hawaii
   C. Kauai
   D. Maui

Canada

■ Resources

The Canadian government maintains tourism offices in several U.S. cities, and through the offices and provincial Web sites, information is readily available.

Canada
www.canada.travel

National parks
www.pc.gc.ca

VIA Rail Canada
www.viarail.ca

Alberta
www.travelalberta.com

Banff National Park
www.banfflakelouise.com

Calgary Stampede
www.calgarystampede.com

Jasper National Park
www.jaspercanadianrockies.com

West Edmonton Mall
www.wem.ca

British Columbia
www.hellobc.com

BC ferries
www.bcferries.bc.ca

BC skiing
www.bcskiing.com

Vancouver
www.tourismvancouver.com

Victoria
www.tourismvictoria.com

Manitoba
www.travelmanitoba.com

New Brunswick
www.newbrunswick.ca

Newfoundland/Labrador
www.newfoundlandandlabrador.com

Northwest Territories
www.spectacularnwt.com

Nova Scotia
www.novascotia.com

Nunavut
www.nunavuttourism.com

Ontario
www.ontariotravel.net

CN Tower
www.cntower.ca

National Gallery of Canada
www.gallery.ca

Niagara Falls
www.tourismniagara.com

Toronto
www.torontotourism.com

Prince Edward Island
www.tourismpei.com

Québec
www.quebecoriginal.com/en

Laurentians
www.laurentides.com/en

Montréal
www.tourisme-montreal.org

Mount Tremblant
www.tremblant.ca/en

Saskatchewan
www.tourismsaskatchewan.com

Yukon
www.travelyukon.com

Kluane National Park
www.canadianparks.com

■ UNESCO World Heritage Sites

For Canada, the UNESCO World Heritage List includes the following:

Cultural Heritage

- Anthony Island, British Columbia
- Head-Smashed-in-Buffalo Jump, Alberta
- Historic area, Québec
- L'Anse aux Meadows Historic Park, Newfoundland
- Lunenburg Old City, Nova Scotia

Natural Heritage

- Canadian Rocky Mountains Parks (Banff and Jasper), British Columbia
- Dinosaur Provincial Park, Alberta
- Gros Morne National Park, Newfoundland
- Miquasha Park, Québec
- Nahanni National Park, Northwest Territories
- Waterton-Glacier International Peace Park, Alberta
- Wood Buffalo National Park, Northwest Territories/Alberta

■ Reading Suggestions: Canada

■ Ken Follett: *Night over Water* (1992) is a thriller set in 1939 on a Pan Am Clipper's flight from England to America, with stops in Canada for history, romance, and adventure.

■ Lucy Maud Montgomery: *Anne of Green Gables* and its sequels contain memories of the author's childhood on Prince Edward Island.

■ Howard Norman: *My Famous Evening: Nova Scotia Sojourns, Diaries & Preoccupations* (2004) tells of haunted houses, ocean birds, and the mysteries of coves, storms, and lives spent close to the sea.

■ Robert William Service: He is known as "the bard of the Yukon" for such poems as "The Shooting of Dan McGrew," from his collection titled *Song of a Sourdough* (1907).

Worksheet 5.1: Geography

_____

Name   Date

Directions: Answer the questions in the space provided.

1. How does permafrost affect any settlement built on it?

   _____

   _____

2. At what time of year should travelers expect to find 24 hours of daylight when they visit a destination in northern Canada?

   _____

3. What is the Canadian Shield?

   _____

   _____

   _____

4. Which Canadian town was chosen by Marconi for his first transatlantic radio transmission? Why did he choose it?

   _____

   _____

   _____

5. Would you recommend the beaches of Prince Edward Island to a family from Pennsylvania seeking a warm-water vacation in July? Justify your answer.

   _____

   _____

   _____

6. You are helping some downhill skiers choose a vacation destination sometime next February. They are trying to decide between a resort in the Laurentians and one in the Rockies. What do you know that might be of help to them?

   _____

   _____

   _____

7. What kind of weather should travelers expect for their trip to the Calgary Stampede?

_____

_____

8. What is the St. Lawrence Seaway?

_____

_____

9. Which is the deepest lake in North America, and where is it located?

_____

10. What is Nunavut?

_____

_____

_____

Worksheet 5.2: Itinerary Planning: Eastern Canada

Name   Date

Sam and Mary Champlain from Louisiana are interested in exploring their French roots. They have about 10 days in August to do so. Grandma Champlain has told Sam that the family came from the town of St. Andrews, New Brunswick, on Passamaquoddy Bay. How would you route them to New Brunswick from Louisiana? How will they get around when they get there? Where will they stay? What is there to see in the area?

Worksheet 5.3: Answering Questions

_____

Name   Date

Directions: How would you respond to travelers who ask the following questions?

1. "We don't speak French. Will we have language difficulties in Québec?"

2. "We are from New England. How does the scenery of western Canada differ from that of the Laurentian Mountains, where we go each year to ski?"

Worksheet 5.4: Map Review

Worksheet 5.4: Map Review

Name _____ Date _____

Directions: Match the destination with its number on the map. Optional: Use industry or online resources to find the airport code of the nearest destination or the nearest airport.

Map Number	Destination	Airport Code
_____	Bay of Fundy	_____
_____	Laurentians	_____
_____	Montréal	_____
_____	Cabot Trail	_____
_____	Churchill and polar bears	_____
_____	Thousand Islands	_____
_____	Toronto	_____
_____	Lake Louise	_____
_____	Ottawa	_____
_____	Niagara Falls	_____
_____	Calgary	_____
_____	Dawson	_____
_____	Saguenay Fjord	_____
_____	Vancouver	_____
_____	L'Anse aux Meadows National Historic Park	_____

Bonus Question: What is the name of the huge body of water in the middle of Canada that almost bisects the country?

_____

Worksheet 5.5: Itinerary Planning: Western Canada

Name   Date

Mr. and Mrs. Lee and their two children, ages 8 and 10, would like your help in planning a driving trip through western Canada. Home for the Lees is San Francisco. What do you suggest?

Worksheet 5.6: Using Reference Materials

Name _____ Date _____

Directions: Using available resources, answer the questions in the space provided. Indicate in your answer what resources you used.

1. What documentation must U.S. leisure travelers have to visit Canada?

   _____

   _____

2. If you exchange U.S. $100 for Canadian money, how many Canadian dollars will you receive?

   _____

3. Will the luxury-loving traveler be happy with accommodations in Montréal? Suggest two hotels.

   _____

   _____

4. The travelers are planning a weekend in Toronto and would like to go when something special is playing in the theaters. What would you suggest?

   _____

   _____

5. Name three tour operators offering motorcoach tours of the Canadian Rockies.

   _____

   _____

   _____

6. What time of year does VIA Rail Canada's cross-country train service operate? How would you make a reservation?

   _____

7. What is the admission fee for Toronto's CN Tower?

   _____

8. A rafting trip down the Alsek River in Kluane National Park and Reserve allows visitors to view the wildlife (including grizzly bears, Dahl sheep, and golden eagles) and glaciers along the way. Permits for rafting on this Canadian Heritage river are strictly limited to one departure per day. How can you help some travelers arrange their trip?

   _____

Worksheet 5.7: Looking Back: A Chapter Quiz

Name _____ Date _____

Directions: Answer the questions in the space provided, or circle the correct answer.

1. What benefits does the landscape of Canada have for tourism?

_____

_____

_____

_____

2. Which is Canada's largest east coast port?

_____

3. What province is known for its festivals of plays by famous authors?

_____

4. Why do they speak French in Québec?

_____

_____

5. What was the Klondike gold rush?

_____

_____

6. What is meant by the term Underground City? What city has a famous one? Why is the concept a particularly good one for a Canadian city?

_____

_____

_____

7. In terms of latitude, Vancouver is closest to
   A. Tokyo, Japan.
   B. Brussels, Belgium.
   C. Lisbon, Portugal.
   D. Stockholm, Sweden.

8. Match the attraction on the left with its location on the right.

_____ Cabot Trail

_____ Athabasca Glacier

_____ Gastown

_____ Rushing tides

_____ Shakespearean Festival

_____ Plains of Abraham

_____ CN Tower

_____ Folklorama

_____ Stampede

_____ Butchart Gardens

A. Toronto

B. Calgary

C. Vancouver Island

D. Québec City

E. Winnipeg

F. Vancouver

G. Cape Breton Island

H. Stratford

I. Icefields Centre

J. Bay of Fundy

Bermuda and the West Indies

■ Resources

Because the choice of a hotel or cruise line is central to satisfaction with an island vacation, hotel guides, tour operators, Web sites, and industry networking become important resources. Choosing accommodations by price alone can ruin a vacation.

Cruise Lines

Azamara Club Cruises
www.azamaraclubcruises.com

Carnival Cruise Lines
www.carnival.com

Celebrity Cruises
www.celebritycruises.com

Costa Cruise Lines
www.costacruise.com

Crystal Cruises
www.crystalcruises.com

Cunard Line
www.cunard.com

Disney Cruise Line
www.disneycruise.com

Holland America Line
www.hollandamerica.com

Moorings (yacht charters)
www.moorings.com

Nicholson's Yachts
www.nicholsonyachts.com

Norwegian Cruise Line
www.ncl.com

Oceania Cruises
www.oceaniacruises.com

Princess Cruises
www.princess.com

Regent Seven Seas
www.rssc.com

Royal Caribbean International
www.royalcaribbean.com

Seabourn Cruise Line
www.seabourn.com

Silversea Cruises
www.silversea.com

Resorts

Beaches
www.beaches.com

Breezes
www.superclubs.com

Club Med
www.clubmed.com

Couples
www.couples.com

Hedonism
www.hedonism.com

Sandals
sandals.com

Islands

Anguilla
www.anguilla-vacation.com

Antigua and Barbuda
www.antigua-barbuda.org

Aruba
www.aruba.com

Bahamas
www.bahamas.com

Atlantis Resort
www.atlantis.com

Harbour Island
www.myharbourislandbahamas.com

UNEXSO
www.unexso.com

Barbados
www.barbados.org

Bermuda
www.gotobermuda.com

Bonaire
www.infobonaire.org

British Virgin Islands
www.bvitourism.com

Cayman Islands
www.caymanislands.ky

Turtle Farm
www.turtle.ky

Curaçao
www.curacao.com/en

Dominica
www.dominica.dm

Dominican Republic
www.domincanrepublic.com

Granada
www.puregranada.com

Guadeloupe
www.guadeloupe-islands.com

Haiti
www.experiencehaiti.org

Jamaica
www.visitjamaica.com

Martinique
us.martinique.org

Montserrat
www.visitmontserrat.com

Puerto Rico
www.seepuertorico.com

Saba
www.sabatourism.com

St. Barthélemy
www.st-barths.com

St. Eustatius (Statia)
www.statiatourism.com

St. Kitts and Nevis
www.stkitts-tourism.kn
www.nevisisland.com

St. Lucia
www.stlucianow.com

St. Maarten
www.st-maarten.com

St. Martin
www.st-martin.org

St. Vincent and Grenadines
www.svgtourism.com

Trinidad and Tobago
www.gotrinidadandtobago.com

Turks and Caicos
www.turksandcaicostourism.com

U.S. Virgin Islands
www.visitusv.com

■ UNESCO World Heritage Sites

For Bermuda and the West Indies, the UNESCO World Heritage List includes the following:

Cultural Heritage

- Brimstone Hill Fortress National Park, St. Kitts and Nevis
- First coffee plantation, Cuba
- La Citadelle, Sans Souci, and Ramiers, Haiti
- La Fortaleza and San Juan historic area, Puerto Rico
- Old Town Havana, Cuba
- Santiago de Cuba, San Pedro de la Roca Castle, Cuba
- St. George town and fortifications, Bermuda
- Santo Domingo colonial city, Dominican Republic
- Trinidad and Valley de los Ingenios, Cuba
- Vitales Valley, Cuba
- Willemstad historic area, Curaçao

Natural Heritage

- Morne Trois Pitons National Park, Dominica
- Parque Nacional Desembarco de Granma, Cuba

■ Reading Suggestions: Bermuda and the West Indies

- Conrad Allen: In *Murder on the Caronia* (2003), ship detectives on Cunard Line's classic old ships solve mysteries at sea. Other books by the same author are *Murder on the Lusitania*, *Murder on the Mauretania*, and *Murder on the Minnesota*.
- Ian Fleming (1908–1964): His spy thrillers featuring James Bond include many Caribbean islands. His former home on Jamaica is a tourist attraction.
- John Grisham: *The Firm* (1991) is a thriller partly set in the Cayman Islands.
- Aarona Booker Kohlman: *Under Tin Roofs* (1993) is a memoir of the author's childhood in the Cayman Islands.
- V. S. Naipaul: *A House for Mr. Biswas* (1961) is a Caribbean classic, written by a Trinidadian novelist, travel writer, and essayist, about a changing Hindu lifestyle.
- Derek Walcott: *Omeros* offers a contemporary odyssey in a Caribbean setting, written by St. Lucia's Nobel Prize–winning poet.
- Herman Wouk: *Don't Stop the Carnival* (1965) is a comedic novel about managing a hotel on a Caribbean island.

Worksheet 6.1: Geography

Name_____ Date_____

Directions: Answer the questions in the space provided. You might have to look back to Chapter 1 for help with some of the answers.

1. What causes waves?

   _____

   _____

   _____

   _____

2. How would you describe the climate of Barbados in July?

   _____

3. Was Cuba ever part of the United States?

   _____

   _____

4. What is Bermuda's weather like in January?

   _____

5. Is Puerto Rico a state?

   _____

6. How did the United States obtain the Virgin Islands?

   _____

   _____

   _____

7. What is the difference between the Greater and Lesser Antilles?

   _____

   _____

   _____

   _____

8. Where are the Windward Islands? Name three.

_____

_____

_____

_____

9. Where are the Leeward Islands? Name three.

_____

_____

_____

_____

10. How are coral islands formed? Name two in the Caribbean.

_____

_____

_____

_____

Worksheet 6.2: Itinerary Planning

_____

Name   Date

A typical island vacation usually lasts 1 week. Mr. and Mrs. Manley are heading to a resort near Ocho Rios in Jamaica. What activities other than sitting in the sun are possible?

Worksheet 6.3: Answering Questions

_____

Name   Date

Directions: How would you respond if travelers asked the following questions?

1. "Isn't a cruise very expensive?"

2. "I've heard that the island is unsafe. Is that true?"

Worksheet 6.4: Map Review

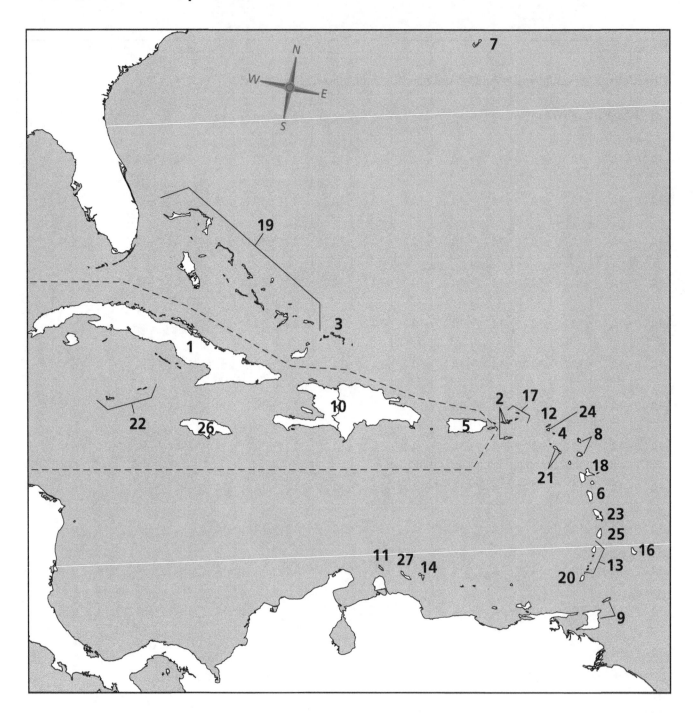

Worksheet 6.4: Map Review

Name _____ Date _____

Directions: Find each number on the map, and then fill in the name of the island next to its number. Optional: Use industry or online resources to find the airport code of the nearest destination or the nearest airport.

Island Name	Airport Code	Island Name	Airport Code
1. _____		15. _____	
2. _____		16. _____	
3. _____		17. _____	
4. _____		18. _____	
5. _____		19. _____	
6. _____		20. _____	
7. _____		21. _____	
8. _____		22. _____	
9. _____		23. _____	
10. _____		24. _____	
11. _____		25. _____	
12. _____		26. _____	
13. _____		27. _____	
14. _____		28. _____	

Worksheet 6.5: Using Reference Materials

Name   Date

Directions: Using available resources, answer the questions in the space provided. Indicate in your answer what resources you used.

1. What are the current documentation requirements for the leisure traveler who wants to visit Barbados?

2. Which islands in the western Caribbean are the ships of Celebrity Cruises visiting this year?

3. Which Jamaican resorts offer all-inclusive vacations?

4. Do ships visiting St. Maarten dock at a pier, or must passengers be tendered to the island?

Worksheet 6.6: Looking Back: A Chapter Quiz

Name _____ Date _____

Directions: Fill in the blanks with the correct word or phrase from the list below.

Atlantic	Caribbean	leeward	tropical
West Indies	windward	from December 15 to April 15	
from June to October	from November to April	golfers	skiers

1. A large number of islands in the _____ are the exposed peaks of an underwater mountain range.

2. The most common type of climate found in the Caribbean is

    _____ .

3. Families with small children seeking calm surf and less exposure to wind should generally seek an island's

    _____ side.

4. Hurricane season in the Caribbean and the East Coast is

    _____ .

5. During winter months (December through April), Bermuda is a popular destination for

    _____ .

6. High season in the Caribbean is _____ .

Directions: Name a country in the Caribbean in which each of the following languages is spoken.

7. Spanish   _____

8. French   _____

9. English   _____

10. Papiamento   _____

11. Hindi   _____

Directions: Write the answer in each blank.

12. Name four islands known for their excellent scuba-diving facilities.

    _____

    _____

13. Which islands are ideal destinations for those seeking to charter a yacht?

_____

_____

_____

14. Which islands would you recommend to couples seeking an all-inclusive resort?

_____

_____

_____

Middle America

■ Resources

Web sites for countries outside the United States are not always in English. Some sites are in the country's official language only. Others give the user a choice of that language or English.

Belize
www.travelbelize.org

Costa Rica
www.visitcostarica.com

Aerial tram
www.rainforestadventure.com

El Salvador
No official site

Guatemala
www.visitguatemala.com/en

Honduras
www.hondurastravel.com/en

Mexico
www.visitmexico.com

Baja California
www.discoverbajacalifornia.com

Cancun
www.cancun.com

Chihuahua Tourism
www.visitmexico.com/en/copper-canyon

Mexico City
www.visitmexico.com/en/mexico-city

Puerto Vallarta
www.visitpuertovallarta.com

Nicaragua
www.visitnicaragua.us

Panama
www.panamatours.com

■ UNESCO World Heritage Sites

For Mexico and Central America, the UNESCO World Heritage List includes the following:

Cultural Heritage

- Campeche fortified town, Mexico
- Chichén Itzá pre-Hispanic city, Mexico
- Guadalajara Hospicio Cabanas, Mexico
- Guanajuato historic town and mines, Mexico
- Leon Viejo ruins, Nicaragua
- Mexico City historic center, Mexico
- Monte Alban archaeological site and Oaxaca center, Mexico
- Palenque pre-Hispanic city and park, Mexico
- Panama City historic district, Panama
- Parque Nacional Tikal, Guatemala
- Popocatépetl monasteries, Mexico
- Portobelo and San Lorenzo fortifications, Panama
- Puebla historic center, Mexico
- Quiriguá archaeological site, El Salvador
- Sierra de San Francisco rock paintings, Mexico
- Teotihuacán pre-Hispanic city, Mexico
- Uxmal pre-Hispanic city, Mexico
- Xochicalco archaeological site, Mexico
- Xochimilco, Mexico
- Zacatecas historic center, Mexico

Natural Heritage

- Area de Conservación Guanacaste, Costa Rica
- Barrier reef, Belize
- Cordillera de Talamanca and Parque Internacional La Amistad, Costa Rica/Panama
- El Vizcaino whale sanctuary, Mexico
- Parque Nacional del Darién, Panama
- Parque Nacional Isla del Coco, Costa Rica
- Parque Nacional Tikal, Guatemala
- *Reserva Biósfera Rio Platano, Honduras
- Reserva Biosfera Sian Ka'an, Mexico

■ Reading Suggestions: Mexico and Central America

- Tony Cohan: *On Mexican Time* (2000) is a memoir of the author's family's expatriate life in San Miguel de Alende, Mexico.

- David McCullough: *The Path between the Seas* (1977) contains gripping narrative, scholarly research, and photographic imagery about the Panama Canal.

- James Michener: *Mexico* (1992) is one of his many novels.

- Samuel Shellabarger: In *Captain from Castile* (1945), Cortez meets the Aztecs. This was made into a swashbuckling film.

- Paul Theroux: *The Mosquito Coast* (1982) is a scathing account of a man's attempt to colonize an inhospitable corner of Central America.

Worksheet 7.1: Geography

Name _____ Date _____

Directions: Answer the questions in the space provided, or circle the correct answer.

1. What is the difference between Central America and Latin America?

   _____

   _____

   _____

2. Which Mexican peninsula separates the Gulf of Mexico from the Caribbean Sea?
   A. Baja
   B. Las Playas
   C. Yucatán
   D. Nicoya

3. Which river forms part of Mexico's border with the United States?
   A. Tepalcatepec
   B. Rio Grande
   C. Panuco
   D. Atengo

4. Mexico has _____ states and 1 federal territory.
   A. 28
   B. 31
   C. 32
   D. 34

5. The Copper Canyon is in Mexico's
   A. south.
   B. north.
   C. east.
   D. west.

6. Many of Mexico's best golf courses are found in
   A. Chihuahua.
   B. Copper Canyon.
   C. Los Cabos.
   D. Colonial Cities.

7. Which of the following is considered a Mexican colonial city, not a resort?
   A. Huatulco
   B. Ixtapa
   C. Guadalajara
   D. Acapulco

8. The largest country in Central America is
   A. Nicaragua.
   B. Guatemala.
   C. Costa Rica.
   D. Panama.

9. The world's second-longest barrier reef is located off the coast of
   A. Costa Rica.
   B. Honduras.
   C. Panama.
   D. Belize.

10. When entering from the Pacific, ships sailing through the Panama Canal sail
    A. northwest.
    B. southeast.
    C. northeast.
    D. southwest.

11. English is the official language in
    A. Costa Rica.
    B. El Salvador.
    C. Belize.
    D. Honduras.

Worksheet 7.2: Itinerary Planning

Name   Date

The Riveras are fascinated by Mexican archaeology. Outline a 10-day trip for them to the Mayan sites of the Yucatán Peninsula.

Worksheet 7.3: Answering Questions

Name _____ Date _____

Directions: How would you respond to travelers who asked the following questions?

1. "My 20-year-old grandson is planning to travel alone to Mexico to visit a friend in Ciudad Ayala. He speaks fluent Spanish but has not traveled in a foreign country. We've heard that Mexico has a lot of crime and want to help him have a safe, enjoyable trip. What do you suggest?"

2. "What do you know about Mexico's Copper Canyon, including the best time to visit, interesting things to see, and available tours?"

Worksheet 7.4: Map Review

Worksheet 7.4: Map Review

_____

Name   Date

Directions: Match the destination listed below with its number on the map. Optional: Use industry or online resources to find the airport code of the nearest destination or the nearest airport.

Map Number   **Airport Code**

_____   Acapulco   _____

_____   Belmopan   _____

_____   Cancún   _____

_____   Copper Canyon   _____

_____   Guatemala City   _____

_____   Los Cabos   _____

_____   Managua   _____

_____   Panama City   _____

_____   San José, Costa Rica _____

_____   San Salvador   _____

_____   Taxco   _____

_____   Tegucigalpa   _____

Bonus Question: What is the name of the body of water between Baja California and the mainland of Mexico?

_____

Worksheet 7.5: Using Reference Materials

Name   Date

Directions: Using available resources, answer the questions in the space provided. Indicate in your answer what resources you used.

1. What health hazards, if any, does the Centers for Disease Control report in Belize?

2. Does the U.S. State Department have any advisories for Central American countries? If so, what are the advisories, and which countries are affected?

3. What are the documentation requirements for a single parent who wants to take a child along on a vacation to Mexico?

4. What can you find out about diving conditions in the Bay Islands of Honduras?

5. What tour companies offer rafting trips in Costa Rica? On what rivers?

Worksheet 7.6: Looking Back: A Chapter Quiz

_____

Name   Date

Directions: Answer the questions in the space provided.

1. Match the civilizations with their areas.

   _____ Aztec   A. Yucatán and Central America

   _____ Olmec   B. Mexico City

   _____ Maya   C. North of Mexico City

   _____ Toltec   D. East coast of Mexico

Directions: Answer the following questions.

2. Which Central American country is most linked with ecotourism and adventure travel?

   _____

3. Is Baja California part of the United States? If not, to which country does it belong?

   _____

   _____

4. Name three important dive destinations in Mexico and Central America.

   _____

   _____

   _____

5. The travelers would like a vacation in the sun, with good beaches and active nightlife. Name three destinations that would suit them.

   _____

   _____

   _____

6. The travelers would like to visit archaeological sites tied to the Mayan culture. Name three in Mexico or Central America.

   _____

   _____

   _____

South America and Antarctica

■ Resources

Lindblad Expeditions
www.expeditions.com

Argentina
www.argentina.travel/en

Buenos Aires
www.turismobuenosaires.gob.ar/en

Bolivia
www.bolivia-usa.org

Brazil
www.visitbrasil.com
(Choose English from dropdown menu.)

Chile
www.chile.travel/en

Easter Island (Rapa Nui)
www.easterislandtourism.com

Colombia
www.colombia.travel/en

Ecuador
www.ecuador.travel

Falkland Islands
www.falklandislands.com

Galápagos Islands
www.discovergalapagos.com

Peru
www.peru.travel/en-us

Machu Picchu
www.machu-picchu.info

■ UNESCO World Heritage Sites

For South America, the UNESCO World Heritage List includes the following:

Cultural Heritage

- Brasilia, Brazil
- Caracas university campus, Venezuela
- Cartegena port, fortress, and monuments, Colombia
- *Chan Chan archaeological area, Peru
- Chavin archaeological site, Peru
- Chiquitos Jesuit missions, Bolivia
- Colonia del Sacramento historic center, Uruguay
- Cordoba Jesuit block and estancias, Argentina
- Cuenca historic center, Ecuador
- Cuzco old city, Peru
- Diamantina historic center, Brazil
- El Fuerte de Sanmaipata, Bolivia
- Jesús and Trinidad Jesuit missions, Paraguay
- Lima historic center, Peru
- Maria Mayor Guarani Jesuit missions, Argentina
- Nazca geoglyphs and Pampas de Juma, Peru (Arequipa historic center, Peru)
- Olinda historic center, Brazil
- Parque Arqueológico San Agustín, Colombia
- Potosí, Bolivia
- Quitó old city, Ecuador
- Salvador de Bahia historic center, Brazil
- Santuario Histórica Machu Picchu, Peru
- São Miguel Jesuit mission ruins, Brazil
- Sucre historic city, Bolivia
- Tiwanaku pre-Hispanic city, Bolivia

Natural Heritage

- Central Surinam Nature Reserve, Surinam
- Discovery Coast Atlantic forest reserves, Brazil
- Pantanal conservation area, Brazil
- Parque Nacional Canaima, Venezuela
- Parque Nacional de Iguazú, Argentina
- Parque Nacional del Manú, Peru
- *Parque Nacional do Iguaçu, Brazil

- Parque Nacional Galápagos, Galápagos Islands
- Parque Nacional Huascarán, Peru
- Parque Nacional Jaú, Brazil
- Parque Nacional Los Glaciares, Argentina
- Parque Nacional Los Katios, Colombia
- Parque Nacional Noel Kempff Mercado, Bolivia
- Parque Nacional Rio Abiseo, Peru
- *Parque Nacional Sangay, Ecuador
- Parque Nacional Serra da Capivara, Brazil
- Parque Nacional Taiampaya & Provincial Ischigualasto, Argentina
- Peninsula Valdés, Argentina
- Santuario Histórico Machu Picchu, Peru
- Southeast Atlantic forest reserves, Brazil

■ Reading Suggestions: South America and Antarctica

- Isabel Allende: She wrote *House of the Spirits* (1981). Allende, a Chilean novelist, short-story writer, and journalist, was touted as the first major female figure of Latin American fiction.
- Hiram Bingham: He wrote *Lost City of the Incas: The Story of Machu Picchu and Its Builders* (1972).
- A. B. Daniel: *Incas—The Gold of Cuzco* (2002) is a trilogy about conquistadors and natives.
- Charles Darwin: *Zoology of the Voyage of the Beagle* (1840) was written after his return from his expedition to the South American coast and Australia.
- Ariel Dorfman: *Desert Memories: Journeys through the Chilean North* (2004) recounts the travels of this Chilean playwright, poet, and novelist into the desert, a land with a tormented history.
- Sir Arthur Conan Doyle: The creator of Sherlock Holmes, he wrote the novel *Lost World* (1912) set in the unexplored mountains of Venezuela, a story about dinosaurs roaming on a tepui's isolated roof.
- Pablo Neruda (1904–1973): This Chilean poet was awarded the Nobel Prize for literature in 1971.
- Antonio Skármeta: *The Postman of Neruda* (1987) was inspiration for the film *Il Postino*.
- Paul Theroux: *The Old Patagonia Express* (1979) tells of a trip from Boston to the tip of South America by train.
- Errol Lincoln Uys: *Brazil* (1986) is a novel of the discovery of Brazil.

Worksheet 8.1: Geography

Name _____   Date _____

Directions: Answer the questions in the space provided.

1. Which is farther east: Santiago, Chile, or Miami, Florida?

   _____

2. Which river carries more water than any other in the world?

   _____

3. What is the world's tallest waterfall, and where can travelers find it?

   _____

4. What are the name and location of the world's highest navigable lake?

   _____

5. What is the Strait of Magellan?

   _____

6. What and where is the Atacama?

   _____

7. What country owns Easter Island? How do you get there?

   _____

8. Which South American country has yet to gain its independence?

   _____

9. Where is Devil's Island? To whom does it belong?

   _____

10. Which is the largest city in the Amazon basin?

    _____

11. Which is the world's highest capital city?

    _____

12. Which is the world's southernmost city?

    _____

Worksheet 8.2: Itinerary Planning

Name   Date

You work for the U.S. State Department and have been given the task of planning the logistics of a business trip for Ricardo Reyes to Santiago, Chile, in August. Mr. Reyes lives in Washington, D.C., and travels on a diplomatic passport. Does he need other documentation? How will you route him? He expects to be in Chile for about 6 weeks, work at the embassy in the city, and have free time on weekends. What suggestions do you have to help him enjoy his trip?

Worksheet 8.3: Answering Questions

Name _____ Date _____

Directions: How would you respond to travelers who asked the following questions?

1. "Rio at Carnival time sounds exciting, but it's such a long trip. Is it worth the trouble?"

2. "What about street crime in Rio?"

Worksheet 8.4: Map Review

Worksheet 8.4: Map Review

Name _____ Date _____

Directions: Match the destination with its number on the map. Optional: Use industry or online resources to find the airport code of the destination or the nearest airport.

Map Number		Airport Code
_____	Angel Falls	_____
_____	Buenos Aires	_____
_____	Cartagena	_____
_____	Galápagos Islands	_____
_____	Iguazú Falls	_____
_____	La Paz	_____
_____	Lake Titicaca	_____
_____	Lima	_____
_____	Manaus	_____
_____	Montevideo	_____
_____	Quito	_____
_____	Rio de Janeiro	_____
_____	Santiago	_____
_____	Tierra del Fuego	_____

Bonus Question: Which South American countries are crossed by the equator?

_____

_____

Worksheet 8.5: Using Reference Materials

Name   Date

Directions: Using available resources, answer the questions in the space provided. Indicate in your answer what resources you used.

1. The Cabrals are planning to visit Rio to see the Carnival festivities. They will stay a week. What are Brazil's documentation requirements for leisure travelers from the United States?

2. From Rio, they would like to make a day trip to Iguazú Falls. Is it possible?

3. What health precautions does the Centers for Disease Control recommend for someone visiting the Amazon rain forest?

4. Ms. Betty Atahualpa has a 2-week vacation coming up this year. She would like to fulfill a dream and see the Inca ruins at Machu Picchu. She just received a tax refund of $2,500. Does she have enough funds for the trip?

Worksheet 8.6: Looking Back: A Chapter Quiz

Name _____ Date _____

Directions: Answer the questions in the space provided.

1. How does the land surface of South America resemble that of North America?

   _____

   _____

2. What mountain range runs along the western coast of South America?

   _____

3. Name South America's highest mountain. Where is it located?

   _____

4. How does a rain forest differ from a jungle?

   _____

   _____

   _____

   _____

5. What are the Pampas? Which country has the largest?

   _____

   _____

6. What is the name of the cold current that flows off South America's Pacific coastline?

   _____

7. What is the language of Brazil?

   _____

8. Which of the Galápagos Islands is the site of the airport?

   _____

9. When is high season in the Galápagos?

   _____

10. What city was the center of the Inca empire?

_____

11. How do you get to Machu Picchu?

_____

_____

_____

12. What is the best time of year to take a cruise around Cape Horn?

_____

13. What are geoglyphs? Give an example in South America.

_____

_____

14. Which South American cities are departure ports for expedition cruises to Antarctica?

_____

_____

_____

The British Isles

■ Resources

VisitBritain is the national tourist office for England, Wales, Scotland, and Northern Ireland, although each division has its own tourist board. The Irish Tourist Board (Bord Failte) fills the function for the Republic of Ireland. When requesting information, you should be as specific as possible.

England
www.visitbritain.com

Albert Dock
www.albertdock.com

Bath/Roman baths
www.romanbaths.co.uk

Big Ben and Parliament
www.parliament.uk

British Museum
www.thebritishmuseum.ac.uk

British Performing Arts
www.whatsonstage.com

Britrail
www.britrail.com

Canterbury Cathedral
www.canterbury-cathedral.org

Castle Howard
www.castlehoward.co.uk

Docklands Museum
www.museumoflondon.org.uk/
  docklands

London Underground
https://tfl.gov.uk/modes/tube

Eurostar
www.raileurope.com

Hadrian's Wall Museum
www.hadrians-wall.org

Hampton Court Palace
www.hrp.org.uk/hampton_court_palace

Harrods
www.harrods.com

Hotelboating
www.hotelboating.co.uk

Inland Waterway Cruises
www.bargeholidayuk.com

London
www.visitlondon.com

London Eye
www.londoneye.com

London Pass
www.londonpass.com

London theater
www.londontheatre.co.uk

National Trust Properties
www.nationaltrust.org.uk

Royal Pavilion/Brighton
brightonmuseums.org.uk/royalpavilion

St. Paul's Cathedral
www.stpauls.co.uk

Salisbury Cathedral
www.salisburycathedral.org.uk

Shakespeare Houses
www.Shakespeare.org.uk

Stonehenge
www.stonehengemasterplan.org

Stratford-upon-Avon
www.shakespearecountry.co.uk

Tate Britain
www.tate.org.uk/britain

Tate Modern
www.tate.org.uk/modern

Victoria & Albert Museum
www.vam.ac.uk

Warwick Castle
www.warwick-castle.co.uk

Westminster Abbey
www.Westminster-abbey.org

Wimbledon tennis
www.wimbledon.org

Windsor Castle
www.royalcollection.org.uk/visit/
    windsorcastle

Yorkshire
www.yorkshire-england.co.uk

Northern Ireland
www.discovernorthernireland.com

Belfast
www.visit-belfast.com

Causeway Coast and Antrim
discovernorthernireland.com/causeway/

Republic of Ireland
www.tourismireland.com

Blarney Castle
www.blarneycastle.ie

Bunratty Castle
www.shannonheritage.com

Dublin
www.visitdublin.com

Guinness Storehouse
www.guinness.com

Irish Country Hotels
www.irishcountryhotels.com

Irish farm holidays
www.irishfarmholidays.com

Scotland
www.visitscotland.com/en-us/

Edinburgh Castle
www.edinburghcastle.gov.uk

Edinburgh Festival
www.eif.co.uk

Scottish castle hotels
www.celticcastles.com

Wales
www.visitwales.com

Brecon Beacons
www.breconbeacons.org

Caernarfon Castle
www.caernarfon-castle.co.uk

Eisteddfod Festivals
www.eisteddfod.org.uk

Snowdonia National Park
www.eryri-npa.gov.uk

Unique properties
www.welshrarebits.co.uk

■ UNESCO World Heritage Sites

For the British Isles, the UNESCO World Heritage List (whc.unesco.org/en/list) includes the following:

Cultural Heritage

- Bath, England
- Blaenavon industrial landscape, Wales
- Blenheim Palace, England
- Canterbury Cathedral, England
- Dorset and East Devon Coast, England
- Edinburgh old and new towns
- Ironbridge Gorge, England
- Maritime Greenwich, England
- Stonehenge, Avebury, and other associated sites, England
- Tower of London, England
- Westminster Abbey and Palace, England

Natural Heritage

- Giants' Causeway, Northern Ireland
- St. Kilda, Scotland

■ Reading Suggestions: The British Isles

Jane Austen once said, "A reader in possession of a good book gains further pleasure from knowing where the author lived, loved, and found inspiration." Her statement inspires literary tours. Tourist centers often have information about authors who lived in their areas and lists of related events.

- R. D. Blackmore: *Lorna Doone, A Romance of Exmoor* (1869) is set in 17th-century Devonshire.

- Charlotte, Emily, and Anne Brontë: Charlotte's *Jane Eyre* (1847) and Emily's *Wuthering Heights* (1847) are considered romance classics.

- Ken Follett: *Pillars of the Earth* (1990) and its sequel, *World Without End* (2007), are the story of the building of a medieval cathedral and a town.

- Winston Graham: He wrote the *Poldark* novels (1945–2002), adventure and romance among 18th-century Cornwall's tin mines.

- Daphne du Maurier: *Rebecca* (1938), *Jamaica Inn* (1936), and *Frenchman's Creek* (1941) offer melodrama, romance, Cornish scenery, and history.

- Thomas Hardy: He wrote eleven Dorsetshire novels (1871–1895), inspiration for countless films.

- James Herriot: *All Creatures Great and Small* (1974), stories of a veterinarian working in the Yorkshire dales, was made into a BBC television series.

- Edward Rutherfurd: He wrote *London* (1997), a story of the city; *Sarum* (1987), based on the history of Salisbury and its cathedral; *The Forest* (2000), a tale of English heritage; and *The Princes of Ireland: The Dublin Saga* (2004), Irish history from the Druids to Henry VIII.

- Leon Uris: *Trinity* (1976) covers a period of Irish history.

- T. H. White: *The Once and Future King* (1958) is about the Arthurian legend.

- Sir Arthur Conan Doyle: Sherlock Holmes stories, first published near the turn of the twentieth century, are still in print in various editions and have been made into films.

- Charles Dickens: *Great Expectations* (1860) setting is London and the Thames. *A Christmas Carol* was popular from its first publication (1843) with stage productions of the book starting within a few months and remain popular today.

- J.K. Rowling: She published the first three children's Harry Potter books in 1999. Her fourth book, *Harry Potter and the Goblet of Fire* (2000) became history's fastest-selling book. *Harry Potter and the Sorcerer's Stone* was the first book made into film (2001).

Worksheet 9.1: Geography

_____ _____
Name   Date

Directions: Answer the questions in the space provided.

1. How would you describe the landscape of the British Isles?

    _____

    _____

2. What makes the White Cliffs of Dover white? What is the geographic term for the chalk and limestone hills that cross the land and form the cliffs?

    _____

    _____

3. Name England's three main land regions.

    _____

    _____

    _____

4. Describe a moor. Where are most of England's moors found?

    _____

    _____

5. Identify Scotland's principal land regions.

    _____

    _____

6. What is Great Britain's highest peak?

    _____

    _____

    _____

7. What is a loch? Where are they found? Which is Scotland's best-known loch?

    _____

    _____

    _____

8. Name three castles in Scotland.

_____

_____

_____

9. The _____ River, the _____ Hills, and the _____ Firth form the border between England and Scotland.

_____

_____

_____

10. What is Ireland's most popular scenic drive mixing picturesque villages and scenic countryside?

_____

_____

11. Name the mother church of the Anglican faith.

_____

_____

12. How would you describe the climate of the British Isles? What sort of clothes would you recommend to someone planning a golf trip to Ireland?

_____

_____

_____

13. Why is the landscape of Wales and Ireland so green?

_____

_____

_____

14. What is GMT?

_____

_____

Worksheet 9.2: Touring Attractions

Name _____ Date _____

Senior citizens and baby boomers account for a large percentage of the market to the British Isles. Many are repeat visitors. The British Isles can satisfy almost every traveler except those who only want to lie on a warm, sunny beach. The questions below test your knowledge of basic information about travel in the British Isles.

Directions: Answer the questions in the space provided.

1. Visitors who want to shop in stores patronized by royalty should look for the

   _____ displayed above a doorway.

2. _____ mark buildings in London where famous people lived or historic events happened.

3. In London, a display of the Crown Jewels can be found in the

   _____ .

4. Although Windsor Castle has been the sovereign's residence since the time of William the Conqueror, the monarch's London home and the site of a daily pageant at its gates in summer is

   _____

5. Where might a traveler seek Camelot?

   _____

6. Do people bathe in Bath? How did the city get its name?

   _____

   _____

7. Name two famous institutions of higher learning in England?

   _____

   _____

8. Eurostar, through the Chunnel, links London to what two European capitals?

   _____

9. What is Hadrian's Wall? Where is it?

   _____

   _____

10. What type of traveler would enjoy a visit to the Channel Islands? Where are the islands located?

_____

_____

11. Edinburgh's Royal Mile connects two important attractions. What are they?

_____

_____

12. Any golfer visiting Scotland would enjoy a visit to the birthplace of golf at _____ .

13. What are Scotland's outer island chains?

_____

_____

14. The rich tradition of Welsh choral music can be found at annual festivals called

_____

15. Ferries sail from Wales to what two points in Ireland?

_____

16. What is one of Northern Ireland's legendary geographic attractions?

_____

17. The principal airport gateways to the Emerald Isle are _____ and

_____ .

18. The Ring of Kerry circles the _____ Peninsula on Ireland's

_____ coast.

19. Name three of Dublin's many attractions.

_____

_____

_____

20. Name three islands off the west coast of Ireland that offer visitors a taste of rural life.

_____

_____

_____

Worksheet 9.3: Itinerary Planning

Name _____ Date _____

Two college students would like to visit London during their winter break when low airfares are a tempting incentive. Their budget is limited. What would you suggest they do during their 1-week trip to the city? How can you help them spend their money wisely? What resources did you use to find the information?

Worksheet 9.4: Answering Questions

_____

Name   Date

Directions: How would you respond to travelers who asked the following questions?

1. "I've heard that England is very expensive. Is there any way to cut costs?"

2. "Should we purchase theater tickets before departing for London? Why or why not?"

Worksheet 9.5: Map Review

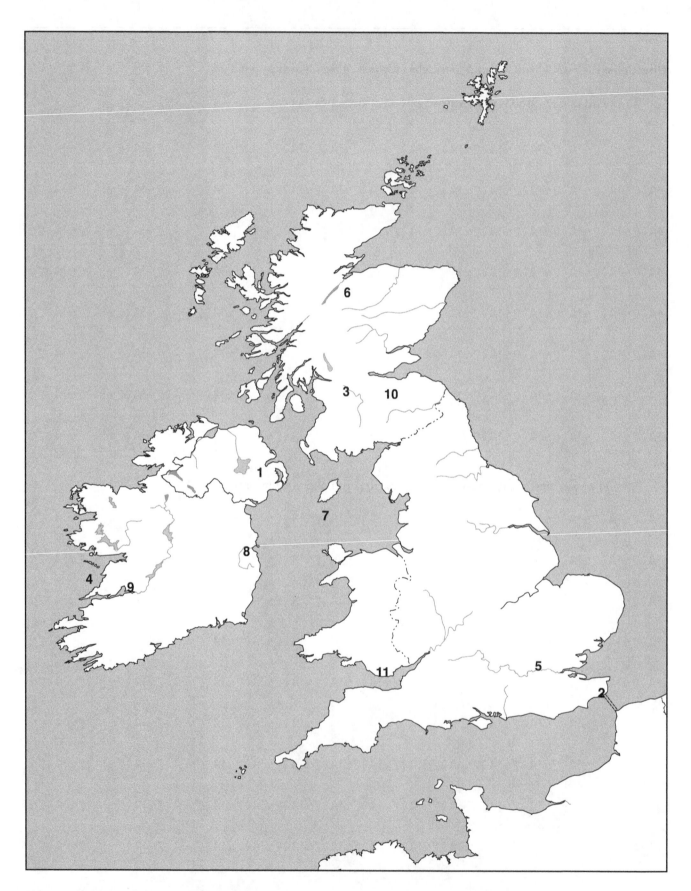

Worksheet 9.5: Map Review

_____

Name   Date

Directions: Match the destination with its number on the map. Optional: Use industry or online resources to find the airport code of the destination or the nearest airport.

Map Number   **Airport Code**

_____   Aran Islands   _____

_____   Belfast   _____

_____   Cardiff   _____

_____   Dover   _____

_____   Dublin   _____

_____   Edinburgh   _____

_____   Glasgow   _____

_____   Inverness   _____

_____   Isle of Man   _____

_____   London   _____

_____   Shannon   _____

Bonus Question: Name two of the four Channel Islands.

_____

_____

Worksheet 9.6: Using Reference Materials

_____

Name   Date

Directions: Using available resources, answer the questions in the space provided. Indicate in your answer what resources you used.

1. What documentation does a leisure traveler from the U.S. need to enter Great Britain?

2. What kinds of rail passes are sold for the British Isles?

3. How much are theater tickets to a top London musical? Where can one buy half-price tickets in London?

4. Travelers want to know the dates of the Edinburgh Festival next summer. Can you help them?

5. Are there any special holiday events in London between Christmas and New Year's Day? Are museums and theaters open?

Worksheet 9.7: Itinerary Planning

Name   Date

The immigrant experience is recent for many Americans, and people of Irish ancestry enjoy going to Ireland to see where their families came from. The Roman Catholic Church has long played a major role in Irish social life. Almost every city has a cathedral with extensive parish records. Plan an 8-day tour for a couple traveling to Ireland to research their roots. Use Web and written resources. Cite sources used.

Worksheet 9.8: Looking Back: A Chapter Quiz

Name _____ Date _____

Directions: Answer the questions in the space provided, or circle the correct answer.

1. What is the Commonwealth?

   _____

   _____

2. Is Northern Ireland an independent country?

   _____

3. Name London's three principal airports, and give their three-letter codes.

   _____

   _____

   _____

4. What range of hills is called "the backbone of England"?

   _____

5. England's longest river is the _____ .

6. Ireland's longest river (and the longest river in the British Isles) is the _____ .

7. Which destination is not part of Great Britain?
   A. Scotland
   B. Northern Ireland
   C. Republic of Ireland
   D. Wales

8. The travelers want to see the circle of stones called Stonehenge. To which city would you direct them to find accommodations?
   A. Plymouth
   B. Salisbury
   C. Portsmouth
   D. Southampton

9. What attraction is out of place in this itinerary?
   A. St. Andrews
   B. Stratford-upon-Avon
   C. Malt Whisky Trail
   D. Balmoral Castle
   E. Edinburgh

10. For each statement, circle either True or False.

   True   False   A moor is heavily forested.

   True   False   William the Conqueror was the last foreign invader of England.

   True   False   Westminster Abbey is the burial place of kings and queens, poets, and heroes.

   True   False   Buckingham Palace is the home of England's prime minister.

   True   False   The Thames is the longest river in the British Isles.

   True   False   An *eisteddfod* is a festival of poetry and music.

   True   False   The Chunnel connects England and the Republic of Ireland.

11. Name the capital and principal city of Wales.

   _____

12. The street that connects Edinburgh Castle and the Palace of Holyroodhouse is called
   A. the Royal Mile.
   B. Princes Street.
   C. Argyll Street.
   D. McDouglass Avenue.

13. The Edinburgh International Festival is held each year during the months of

   _____.

14. In Dublin, at Trinity College, visitors can see the famous literary masterpiece, the

   _____.

15. Travelers can kiss the Blarney Stone in southwest Ireland when they visit the city of

   _____.

Northern Europe

■ Resources

Tourist boards, publications, and industry sources offer a wealth of information about northern Europe. Travelers tend to underestimate distances, traffic, and crowds in Europe. As a result, they often wind up spending more time on the road or waiting around than in actual sightseeing. A tour operator's brochure can help when you are unfamiliar with a destination and need to determine how much distance can be traveled per day.

Transportation

Auto Europe
www.autoeurope.com

Europcar
www.europcar.com

European rail
www.raileurope.com

River cruises
www.amawaterways.com
www.vikingrivercruises.com

Austria

www.austria.info

Castle hotels
www.schlosshotels.co.at

Schonbrunn Palace
www.schoenbrunn.at

Vienna
www.wien.info

Belgium

www.visitbelgium.com

Denmark

www.visitdenmark.com

Copenhagen
www.visitcopenhagen.dk

Finland

www.gofinland.org

Germany

www.germany.travel

Castle hotels
www.burghotel.de

Iceland

www.visiticeland.com

Farm holidays
www.farmholidays.is

Reykjavik
www.visitreykjavik.is

Liechtenstein

(see Switzerland)

Luxembourg
www.visitluxembourg.com

The Netherlands
www.holland.com

Anne Frank House
www.annefrank.org

Van Gogh Museum
www.vangoghmuseum.nl/en

Norway
www.visitnorway.com

Coastal voyages
www.hurtigruten.us

Sweden
www.visitsweden.com

Göta Canal
www.gotakanal.se/en

Switzerland
www.myswitzerland.com

Lake Geneva
www.lake-geneva-region.ch

Matterhorn
www.myswitzerland/en-us/
    zermatt.html

Swiss Rail
www.sbb.ch/en

■ UNESCO World Heritage Sites

For northern Europe, the UNESCO World Heritage List includes the following:

Cultural Heritage

- Aachen (Aix-la-Chapelle) Cathedral, Germany
- Amsterdam, the Netherlands: defense line
- Beemster Polder, the Netherlands
- Belfries of Flanders and Wallonia, Belgium
- Bergen, Norway: Bryggen (wharf)
- Berlin, Germany: museums, including the Pergamon
- Berne, Switzerland: old city
- Bruges, Belgium: historic center
- Brussels, Belgium: Grand-Place
- Cologne Cathedral, Germany
- Dessau and Weimar, Germany: Bauhaus buildings
- Drottingholm Slot (royal palace), Sweden
- Eisleben and Wittenberg, Germany: Luther memorials
- Flemish Béguinages, Belgium
- Graz, Austria: historic center
- Hallstatt-Dachstein-Salzkammergut, Austria: cultural landscape
- Helsinger (Elsinore), Denmark: Kronborg Castle
- Helsinki (Helsingfors), Finland: Suomenlinna Sea Fortress
- Kinderdijk-Elshout, the Netherlands: windmills
- Lübeck, Germany: Hanseatic city

- Luxembourg City, Luxembourg: old town and fortifications
- Salzburg, Austria: historic center, Mozart's birthplace, residence
- Semmering Railway, Austria
- Speyer, Germany: cathedral
- Stockholm, Sweden: Skogskykogarden
- Trier, Germany: Roman monuments
- Urmes stave church, Norway
- Utrecht, the Netherlands
- Vienna, Austria: Schloss Schönbrunn and gardens
- Visby, Sweden: Hanseatic town and Viking site
- Weimar, Germany: classical city
- Würzburg, Germany: Residenz with the court palaces and square

Natural Heritage

- High Coast, Sweden
- Lapponian area, Sweden
- Messel Pit fossil site, Germany

■ Reading Suggestions: Northern Europe

- Hans Christian Andersen (1805–1875): He is internationally known for his fairy tales. Copenhagen's *Little Mermaid* statue is one of the city's most popular attractions.

- Michael Gorra: *The Bells in Their Silence: Travel through Germany* (2004) is a humorous interpretation of modern Germany.

- Christopher Isherwood: *Berlin Stories* (1946) contains stories of social corruption inspired by his life in Germany during Hitler's rise to power and is the basis for the Broadway musical *Cabaret*.

- Stieg Larsson: *The Girl with the Dragon Tattoo* (2008), *The Girl Who Played with Fire* (2009) and *The Girl Who Kicked the Hornet's Nest* (2010) are Swedish crime novels made into films.

- Helen MacInnes: She wrote *The Salzburg Connection* (1963), a thriller.

- Herman Wouk: His novels *The Winds of War* (1971) and *War and Remembrance* (1978), the story of World War II in Europe and the Pacific, were made into a TV mini-series.

Worksheet 10.1: Geography

Name _____   Date _____

Directions: Answer the questions in the space provided.

1. Name the northern European capital with a famous pedestrian-only street.

   _____

2. Active volcanoes, hot springs, and spouting geysers are attractions of _____ .

3. The mountain system dominating the southern part of northern Europe is the _____ .

4. The mountain range that separates Norway and Sweden is _____ .

5. The two peninsulas that dominate northern Europe are the _____ Peninsula

   and the _____ Peninsula.

6. How does the term "Land of the Midnight Sun" affect the traveler?

   _____

7. Describe where the Rhine River flows, from start to finish. What is the most scenic part of the river?

   _____

   _____

   _____

   _____

8. The Danube River flows in a(n) _____ direction to the

   _____ Sea.

9. What causes northern Europe to have a generally milder climate than parts of North America at the same latitude?

   _____

   _____

10. How would you describe the landscape of Finland?

    _____

    _____

11. The _____ Sea separates the European mainland from Great Britain.

12. The _____ Sea separates Sweden from the northern Europe mainland.

Worksheet 10.2: Itinerary Planning

Name   Date

Mr. and Mrs. Schulse are planning a trip to Germany. They want to see King Ludwig's castles, travel the Romantic Road, and perhaps spend a few days at the Oktoberfest. How should you route them? When should they go?

Worksheet 10.3: Answering Questions

_____
Name   Date

Directions: How would you respond to travelers who asked the following questions?

1. "My wife and I will be celebrating our 25th anniversary in Vienna, Austria. Can you recommend any restaurants—not necessarily pricey—that specialize in Viennese cuisine for an anniversary dinner?"

2. "We went to Alaska last summer. Isn't a trip to Scandinavia much the same?"

3. "I've heard that the Nordic countries can be very expensive. Is this true?"

4. "We'd like to go on a river cruise, but won't it be frustrating floating by interesting towns when we want to stop and explore?"

Worksheet 10.4: Map Review

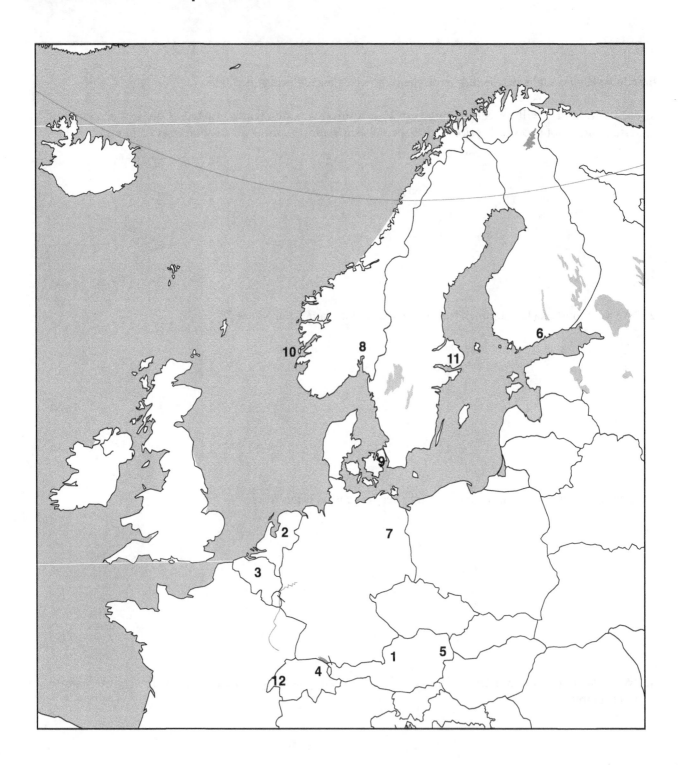

Worksheet 10.4: Map Review

_____

Name   Date

Directions: Fill in the blanks.

Match the destination with its number on the map. You can use each number only once. Optional: Use industry or online resources to find the airport code of the destination or the nearest airport.

Map Number   **Airport Code**

_____   Amsterdam   _____

_____   Bergen   _____

_____   Berlin   _____

_____   Brussels   _____

_____   Copenhagen   _____

_____   Geneva   _____

_____   Helsinki   _____

_____   Oslo   _____

_____   Salzburg   _____

_____   Stockholm   _____

_____   Vienna   _____

_____   Zürich   _____

Bonus Question: Northern Europe is located in the _____ and the

_____ Hemispheres.

Worksheet 10.5: Using Reference Materials

Name _____ Date _____

Directions: Using available resources, answer the questions in the space provided. Indicate in your answer what resources you used.

1. The travelers have taken many trips to Europe but have never been to Belgium or Luxembourg. They are inquiring about train service. How long does it take by train from Paris to Brussels and from Luxembourg City back to Paris?

2. What documentation does the leisure traveler need to enter Finland?

3. The travelers would like tickets to next year's Salzburg Festival. What can you find out about availability and price?

4. What are the embarkation points and attractions of Rhine River cruises? What is the price of an average cabin with a balcony per person, double occupancy for a 7-day cruise?

Worksheet 10.6: Looking Back: A Chapter Quiz

Name _____   Date _____

Directions: Answer the questions in the space provided, or circle the correct answer.

1. What is the European Union?

   _____

   _____

2. Match the country with its capital. Add the city's three-letter airport code.

Capital	Capital's Airport Code	Country	
_____	_____	Belgium	A. Berlin
_____	_____	Denmark	B. Oslo
_____	_____	Finland	C. Stockholm
_____	_____	Germany	D. Luxembourg City
_____	_____	Iceland	E. Berne
_____	_____	Liechtenstein	F. Amsterdam
_____	_____	Luxembourg	G. Brussels
_____	_____	The Netherlands	H. Helsinki
_____	_____	Norway	I. Copenhagen
_____	_____	Sweden	J. Reykjavik
_____	_____	Switzerland	K. Vaduz

3. What are the two cultural groups that make up Belgium?

   _____

   _____

4. Travelers wanting to see Norway's fjord coast while traveling on board a coastal steamer should head to the embarkation city of
   A. Oslo.
   B. Trondheim.
   C. Tromsø.
   D. Bergen.

5. Copenhagen's best-known small landmark is the
   A. Lur Blowers.
   B. Little Mermaid.
   C. Radhuspladsen.
   D. Sailor's Memorial.

6. The best clothing advice to give a summer traveler to northern Europe is to bring
   A. jogging clothes.
   B. for men, a suit with a tie; for women, a skirt and blouse.
   C. comfortable shoes, layered clothing, and an umbrella.
   D. shorts and sleeveless tops.

7. The capital city of the European Union is
   A. Amsterdam.
   B. Brussels.
   C. Berlin.
   D. Zürich.

8. To see alpine scenery such as filmed in *The Sound of Music*, travelers should visit Austria and the city of
   A. Salzburg.
   B. Vienna.
   C. Innsbrück.
   D. Kitzbühel.

9. The most scenic part of a Rhine River cruise is between
   A. Mainz and Cologne.
   B. Heidelberg and Frankfurt.
   C. Baden-Baden and Heidelberg.
   D. Bonn and Cologne.

10. One of Brussels's famous attractions is the beautiful medieval square called the
    A. Casemates.
    B. Lower City.
    C. Grand' Place.
    D. Centrum.

11. Travelers wanting to see Holland's polders, windmills, people wearing wooden shoes, and cheese markets should head to
    A. Haarlem and Lisse.
    B. Volendam and Alkmaar.
    C. Scheveningen.
    D. Delft and The Hague.

12. Which is not a castle in Germany?
    A. Oberammergau
    B. Neuschwanstein
    C. Linderhof
    D. Herrenchiemsee

Eastern Europe

■ Resources

Tour operators who deal with Eastern Europe on a daily basis are usually good sources of logistical information if you are making a booking with their organization. For other help, turn to the tourist boards.

Transportation
European rail
www.raileurope.com

Belarus
www.belarus.by/en

Bulgaria
www.bulgariatravel.org

Czech Republic
www.czechtourism.com

Prague
www.praguecitytourism.cz/en

Estonia
www.visitestonia.com

Tallinn
www.visittallinn.ee

Hungary
www.gotohungary.com

Latvia
www.latvia.travel/en

Lithuania
www.lithuania.travel/en-gb/

Moldova
www.moldova.org

Poland
www.poland.travel/en

Romania
www.romaniatourism.com

Russia
www.russia-travel.com

Slovakia
www.slovakia.travel/en

Slovenia
www.slovenia.info

Ukraine
www.travelukraine.org

■ UNESCO World Heritage Sites

For Eastern Europe, the UNESCO World Heritage List includes the following:

Cultural Heritage

- Auschwitz-Birkenau concentration camp, Poland
- Budapest, Hungary: banks of the Danube and Buda Castle
- Cesky Krumlov, Czech Republic: historic center
- Coronian Spit, Lithuania
- Ferapontov Monastery, Russia
- Holasovice historic village reservation, Czech Republic
- Hollokö, Slovak Republic: traditional village
- Ivanova, Bulgaria: rock chapels
- Kazan Kremlin: Russia
- Kazanluk: Thracian tomb, Bulgaria
- Khizi Pogost, Russia
- Kiev, Ukraine, St. Sophia Cathedral and Lavra of Kyiv-Pechersk
- Kraków historic center, Poland
- Malbork, Poland: Teutonic castle
- Maramures, Romania: wooden churches
- Mir, Belarus: castle complex
- Moldavian churches, Romania
- Moscow, Russia: Church of the Ascension at Kolomenskoye
- Moscow, Russia: Kremlin, Red Square, and St. Basil's Cathedral
- Novgorod, Russia: historic monuments and surroundings
- Prague, Czech Republic: historic center
- Riga, Latvia: historic center
- Rila, Bulgaria: monastery
- St. Petersburg, Russia: historic center with Hermitage Museum
- Sighisoara, Romania: historic center
- Solovetskiye Ostrova cultural and historic area, Russia
- St. Petersburg, Russia: historic center with Hermitage Museum
- Sveshtari, Bulgaria: Thracian tomb
- Tallinn, Estonia: historic center
- Vilnius, Lithuania: old city
- Vlkolinec, Slovak Republic
- Warsaw, Poland: historic center
- Wieliczka, Poland: salt mines

Natural Heritage

- Aggtalek Caves and the Slovak karst, Hungary/Slovak Republic

- Bialowieza Forest, Poland/Belarus

- Danube Delta, Romania

- Golden Mountains of Altay, Russia

- Kamchatka volcanoes, Russia

- Komi virgin forests, Russia

- Lake Baikal, Russia

- Pirin National Park, Bulgaria

- *Srebarna Nature Reserve, Bulgaria

- Western Caucasus, Russia

■ Reading Suggestions: Eastern Europe

Travelers to Eastern Europe benefit from background reading. Much of the history and many of the sites are unknown to the typical tourist.

- Anne Applebaum: *Gulag: A History* (2004) tells of the origins and evolution of the notorious labor camps in post-revolutionary Russia.

- Stephanie Elizondo Griest: *Around the Bloc: My Life in Moscow, Beijing, and Havana* (2004) recounts a university student's year abroad in Moscow and gives a tour of what's left of the communist bloc.

- Robert K. Massie: *Nicholas and Alexandra* (1967) is a story of the last tsar and his family.

- James Michener: *Poland* (1983) blends history and fiction.

- Simon Sebag Montefiore: *Stalin: The Court of the Red Tsar* (2004) provides a portrait of the dictator fashioned from newly opened archives.

- Boris Pasternak: *Doctor Zhivago* (1957) won a Nobel Prize, which Pasternak had to reject because of the furor the novel triggered in the Soviet Union.

- Edward Rutherfurd: Like Michener, Rutherfurd makes his fictional characters take second place to historical events in *Russka* (1991).

- Alexander Solzhenitsyn: *The Gulag Archipelago* (1973) details the terror of Stalin's reign.

- Bram Stoker: *Dracula* (1897) is a novel about vampires in Transylvania and England.

Worksheet 11.1: Geography

Name _____   Date _____

Directions: Answer the questions in the space provided.

1. What is Eastern Europe's dominant geographic feature?

   _____

2. Name the Baltic States. Why do they have that name?

   _____

   _____

   _____

3. Where does Asia start and Europe end?

   _____

   _____

4. What are the steppes? Where in Eastern Europe are they found?

   _____

   _____

5. Europe's longest river, the Volga, begins southeast of _____

   and flows south to the _____ Sea.

6. What sort of weather should the traveler expect when visiting Moscow in the summer?

   _____

7. Which Baltic country is closest to Finland and is often visited on 1-day tours from Helsinki?

   _____

8. What natural resource has attracted tourists to the Czech cities of Carlsbad and Marienbad for centuries?

   _____

9. Most of eastern Hungary is an area of great plains called the _____ .

10. Eastern Russia is the site of the world's deepest lake, Lake _____ .

11. Name three Eastern European countries bordering the Black Sea.

   _____

Worksheet 11.2: Itinerary Planning

Name   Date

Mr. and Mrs. Vaclav Lepescu request your help. They plan to fly into Munich, want to rent a car there and drive to Prague, and then plan to visit Vienna before heading back to Munich. Mr. Lepescu says: "I've heard that driving into the Czech Republic may be difficult and expensive, but we enjoy the freedom of stopping along the way and doing our own thing." What can you find out about auto rental in the area? How would you route the couple?

Worksheet 11.3: Answering Questions

Name   Date

Directions: How would you respond to travelers who asked the following questions?

1. "How do most people travel across Russia? Is it possible to drive?"

2. "I've heard the hotels in Russia are like barracks. Is that true?"

3. "We want to explore on our own and try the Moscow Metro, but we don't know how to deal with the unfamiliar alphabet. What can we do?"

Worksheet 11.4: Map Review

Worksheet 11.4 Map Review

Name _____ Date _____

Directions: Match the destination with its number on the map. Optional: Use industry or online resources to find the airport code of the destination or the nearest airport.

Map Number   **Airport Code**

_____   Bratislava   _____

_____   Bucharest   _____

_____   Budapest   _____

_____   Kiev   _____

_____   Minsk   _____

_____   Moscow   _____

_____   Prague   _____

_____   Riga   _____

_____   St. Petersburg   _____

_____   Sofia   _____

_____   Tallinn   _____

_____   Vilnius   _____

_____   Warsaw   _____

Bonus Question: It is 1700 standard time in your hometown. What time is it in Moscow?

_____

Worksheet 11.5: Using Reference Materials

_____
Name   Date

Directions: Using available resources, answer the questions in the space provided. Indicate in your answer what resources you used.

The travelers are planning an independent trip in July to visit relatives in Moscow.

1. How would you route them by air from your home to their destination?

2. What documentation do they need?

3. Are there any health concerns? If so, what are they?

4. Their relatives' apartment is too small for guests. Where would they stay in Moscow?

5. Do you have any suggestions for sightseeing? They would like to see the Bolshoi Ballet. Is this possible?

Worksheet 11.6: Looking Back: A Chapter Quiz

Name _____ Date _____

Directions: Answer the following questions.

1. Match the Eastern European attraction with its city.

_____	Budapest	A. Kremlin
_____	Czestochowa	B. Hermitage Museum
_____	Kraków	C. Song festivals
_____	Moscow	D. Royal Palace on Wawel Hill
_____	Prague	E. Black Madonna
_____	St. Petersburg	F. Wilanow Palace
_____	Tallinn	G. Charles Bridge
_____	Warsaw	H. Fishermen's Bastion

2. Mark each statement True or False.

True	False	European spas offer health treatments.
True	False	Lithuania is the most developed of the Baltic States.
True	False	Russian people are all of the same ethnic background.
True	False	The Czech Republic is ready for tourism.
True	False	Moscow's winters are mild and its summers cold.
True	False	The Danube Bend is between Esztergom and Visegrád.
True	False	Eastern cuisine is heavy on salads and light on meat and potatoes.
True	False	GUM on Red Square is a large department store.
True	False	St. Petersburg is Russia's second-largest city, with famous museums and palaces.

Southern Europe

■ Resources

Transportation

European rail
www.raileurope.com

Albania
www.albaniantourism.com

Andorra
www.turisme.ad

Bosnia-Herzegovina
www.mvp.gov.ba

Croatia
www.croatia.hr

Cyprus
www.visitcyprus.org

France
www.franceguide.com

Balloon trips
www.bombardsociety.com

Chenonceaux
www.chenonceau.com

Corsica
www.visit-corsica.com

Macedonia
None

Eiffel Tower
www.tour-eiffel.fr

French Country Waterways
www.fcwl.com

Gites de France
www.gites-de-france.fr

Louvre
www.louvre.fr

Paris
www.paris-touristoffice.com

Versailles
www.chateauversailles.fr

Gibraltar
www.gibraltar.gov.gil

Greece
www.gnto.gr

Italy
www.italiantourism.com

Farmhouse rentals
www.agriturist.it

Spas
www.spas.it

Trains
www.trenitalia.com

Villas
www.italianvillas.com

Malta

www.visitmalta.com

Monaco

www.visitmonaco.com

Montenegro

montenegro.travel

Portugal

www.visitportugal.com

Gulbenkian
www.museu.gulbenkian.pt/museu/en/
 Homepage

Pousadas
www.pousadas.pt

Serbia

serbia.travel

Spain

www.spain.info

Guggenheim Bilbao
www.guggenheim-bilbao.es/en

La Sagrada Familia
www.sagradafamilia.org/en

Paradors
www.parador.es/en

Vatican City

www.vaticanstate.va

Yugoslavia

www-gewi.uni-graz.at/tourism

■ UNESCO World Heritage Sites

For southern Europe, the UNESCO World Heritage List includes the following:

Cultural Heritage

- Agrigento, Sicily, Italy: archaeological area

- Alberobello, Italy: Trulli houses

- Altamira, Spain: caves and archaeological site

- Amalfi Coast, Italy

- Assisi, Italy: sites associated with St. Frances

- Athens, Greece: Acropolis

- Avignon, France: Palace of the Popes

- Barcelona, Spain: Parque and Palacio Güell and Casa Milá

- Canal du Midi, France

- Carcassonne, France: historic fortified city

- Chambord, France: chateaux and estate

- Chartres, France: cathedral

- Cinque Terre, Italy: Portovénere

- Córdoba, Spain: mosque and historic center

- Delphi, Greece: archaeological site

- Dubrovnik, Croatia: old city

- El Escorial, Spain: palace and monastery

- Epidaurus, Greece: archaeological site
- Évora, Portugal: historic center
- Florence, Italy: historic center, Duomo, Uffizi, and Ponte Vecchio
- Fontainebleau, France: palace and park
- Granada, Spain: Alhambra, Generalife, and Albaicín quarter
- Hadrian's Villa, Italy
- Vallée du Vézère, France: Lascaux and other grottoes
- Loire Valley, between Chalonnes and Sully-sur-Loire, France
- Malta, Ggantija: megalithic temples
- Météora, Greece: rock monasteries
- Milan, Italy: *The Last Supper*
- Mont-St-Michel and its bay, France
- Naples, Italy: historic center
- Olympia, Greece: archaeological site
- Paris, France: banks of the Seine, Eiffel Tower, Louvre, Musée d'Orsay, and Notre-Dame
- Pisa, Italy: Piazza del Duomo and Leaning Tower
- Pompeii, Herculaneum, and Torre Annunziata, Italy: archaeological areas
- Porto (Oporto), Portugal: historic center
- Ravenna, Italy: early Christian monuments and mosaics
- Reims, France: Cathedral Notre-Dame
- Rhodes, Greece: medieval city
- Rome, Italy: historic center
- San Gimignano, Italy: historic center and towers
- Sardinia, Italy: Su Nuraxi di Barúmini
- Segovia, Spain: old town and aqueduct
- Seville, Spain: cathedral, Alcazar, and Archivo de Indias
- Siena, Italy: historic center, Piazza del Campo
- Sintra, Portugal: historic city
- Split, Croatia: historic center with Diocletian palace
- Tarragona, Spain Roman city
- Toledo, Spain: historic city
- Valletta, Malta: old city
- Vatican City, Italy
- Venice, Italy: lagoon and Basilica di San Marco
- Verona, Italy: historic city
- Versailles, France: palace and park
- Vicenza, Italy: city and Palladian villas of the Veneto

- Way of St. James pilgrimage route (Camino de Santiago) through France and Spain

Natural Heritage

- Athens, Greece
- Banks of the Seine: Paris, France
- Durmitor National Park, Serbia and Montenegro
- Golfe de Girolate and Reserve Naturelle, Corsica, France
- Ibiza, Spain: biodiversity and culture
- Ísole Eólie (Lipari), Italy
- *Kotor and its gulf, Serbia and Montenegro
- Laurisilva of Madeira, Portugal
- Metéora, Greece
- Mont Perdu/Monte Pedido, France/Spain
- Mont-Saint-Michel and its bay, France
- Ohrid Lake region, Macedonia
- Parque Nacional coto de Doñana, Spain
- Parque Nacional de Garajonay, Gomera, Canary Islands, Spain
- Plitvice Lakes National Park, Croatia
- Skocjan Caves, Slovenia

■ Reading Suggestions: Southern Europe

- Carol Drinkwater: *Olive Season* (2003) is a romance set in Provence, France.
- Lawrence Durrell (1912–1990): His fiction and non-fiction books are about the Mediterranean and Aegean islands, where Durrell lived and worked for many years for the British Foreign Office.
- Umberto Eco: *The Name of the Rose* (1980) is a medieval mystery.
- E. M. Forster: *A Room with a View* (1961) is a novel about Florence and the English.
- Robert Harris: *Pompeii* (2004) is a novel to read before, while, or instead of traveling to the ruins.
- Ernest Hemingway: *For Whom the Bell Tolls* (1940) is a novel based on the author's experiences in Spain during the Spanish Civil War.
- Washington Irving: *Legends of the Alhambra* (1832–1852) is a story about the clashes between the Spaniards and the Moors, written while Irving was an attaché at the American legation in Madrid.
- Nikos Kazantzakis: *Zorba the Greek* (1946) is a novel that was turned into a

film and Broadway musical.

- Frances Mayes: *Under the Tuscan Sun* (1996) is a memoir of a house restoration in Tuscany.

- Peter Mayle: *A Year in Provence* and *Toujours Provence* (1971) are about an English couple building a house in the south of France. *A Good Year* (2004) is also about France.

- James Michener: *The Drifters* (1971) is a novel about six runaways adrift in Spain, Marrakesh, and Mozambique.

- Daphne Phelps: In *A House in Sicily* (1999), the author falls in love with a house, a community, and a way of life.

- Sidney Sheldon: *Other Side of Midnight* (1973), a story of tycoons, Paris, D.C., and a villa on a Greek island, was a best-seller and eventually a movie.

- Patrick Süskind: *Perfume* (1986) is a medieval detective story about the "nose" needed for perfume development.

- Emma Tennant: *A House in Corfu* (2002) details the delights and frustrations of a family's daily life on a Greek island.

Worksheet 12.1: Geography

Name _____   Date _____

Directions: Answer the questions in the space provided.

1. What do people mean when they say a destination has a "Mediterranean climate"?

   _____

   _____

2. Southern Europe has three large peninsulas. Name them.

   _____

   _____

   _____

3. What is the name of the strait that connects the Mediterranean Sea and the Atlantic Ocean?

   _____

4. Portugal's and Spain's southern coasts are well known to vacationers. In Portugal, this coastal area is the

   _____.

   In Spain, the region is called the

   _____.

5. Which Mediterranean island is the most easterly?

   _____

   Which island is the largest?

   _____

   Which ones belong to Spain?

   _____

   Which one belongs to France?

   _____

6. Name the mountain range that separates Spain from France.

   _____

7. The mountains that form the spine of Italy are the

_____.

8. Name at least five popular Greek islands.

_____

_____

_____

_____

_____

_____

9. The river running through the heart of Paris is the Seine, but France's longest river, which is most famous for its châteaux, castles, and scenery, is the

_____.

10. The Isthmus of Corinth connects mainland Greece to the _____ Peninsula.

11. Why is Cyprus divided?

_____

_____

12. Where is the Rock of Gibraltar? Which country controls it? Which country wants it?

_____

_____

_____

_____

Worksheet 12.2: Itinerary Planning

_____
Name   Date

Salvatore de Trevi wants a bike trip through Italy. He is willing to consider a tour group, but hopefully one that caters to young single travelers. Do you have any suggestions as to region and routing?

Worksheet 12.3: Answering Questions

_____

Name   Date

Directions: How would you respond to travelers who asked the following questions?

1. "I'm planning a trip to Greece. Would travel insurance cover a cancellation in case of a U.S. State Department recommendation against nonessential travel or a terrorist attack there?"

2. "I want to see the Sistine Chapel, but is there any way to avoid the crowds?"

Worksheet 12.4: Map Review

Worksheet 12.4: Map Review

Name _____ Date _____

Directions: Match the destination with its corresponding number on the map. Optional: Use industry or online resources to find the airport code of the destination or the nearest airport.

Map Number		Airport Code
_____	Athens	_____
_____	Barcelona	_____
_____	Crete	_____
_____	Cyprus	_____
_____	Florence	_____
_____	Lisbon	_____
_____	Madrid	_____
_____	Milan	_____
_____	Mykonos	_____
_____	Naples	_____
_____	Nice	_____
_____	Paris	_____
_____	Rome	_____
_____	Venice	_____

Bonus Question: How many time zones are there in southern Europe?

Worksheet 12.5: Using Reference Materials

Name   Date

Directions: Using available resources, answer the questions in the space provided. Indicate in your answer what resources you used.

1. The travelers are planning an independent trip to France in the spring. How would you route them by air from your city?

2. What documentation do they need to enter France?

3. They have a limited budget. Where could they stay in Paris?

4. What suggestions do you have for 3 days of city sightseeing?

Worksheet 12.6: Looking Back: A Chapter Quiz

_____

Name   Date

Directions: Answer the questions in the space provided, or circle the correct answer.

1. The two small independent countries within Italy are _____

   and _____ .

2. Match each description with its museum by writing the letter of the correct description in the blank.

   _____ Uffizi   A. Museum in Paris, the largest in the world

   _____ Vatican   B. Museum in Madrid with works by Spanish masters

   _____ Prado   C. Museum with the world's largest religious collection

   _____ Louvre   D. Museum with the art collection in Florence

3. The World War II D-Day beaches are found in the French province of _____ .

4. Europe's largest medieval fortress can be explored at _____ .

5. Accommodations in Spain include the _____ , a network of state-owned and -operated hotels.

6. One of Barcelona's favorite sons is architect
   A. Jose Sert.
   B. Andrés Segovia.
   C. Antoni Gaudí.
   D. Miguel de Cervantes.

7. The Alhambra is found in _____ .

8. The so-called capital of the Algarve and the site of its airport is _____ .

9. Name the southern European country whose heads of state are the president of France and the bishop of Urgell.

   _____

10. Italy's largest lake is _____ .

11. The oldest quarter of Athens, with restaurants and bars providing activity until late at night, is called the

    _____ .

12. For each statement, circle True or False.

    True   False   Landmarks in Rome include the Doge's Palace, St. Mark's Square, and the Murano glass-working center.

    True   False   Southern Greece consists of the flat Peloponnese Peninsula.

True	False	The Mediterranean cruise season begins around Easter and continues until early October.
True	False	Piraeus is the port of Athens.
True	False	Rhodes is the largest of the Greek islands.

Africa and the Middle East

■ Resources

Botswana
www.botswanatourism.co.bw

Egypt
www.egypt.travel

Israel
www.goisrael.com

Morocco
www.muchmorocco.com

Namibia
www.namibiatourism.co.uk

South Africa
www.countrysouthafrica.net

Blue Train
www.bluetrain.co.za

Cape Town
www.capetown.travel

Rovos Rail
www.rovos.com

Tanzania
www.tanzaniatouristboard.com

Turkey
www.tourismturkey.org

Zambia
www.zambiatourism.com

Zambezi Swing
www.thezambeziswing.com

Zimbabwe
www.zimbabwetourism.co.zw

■ UNESCO World Heritage Sites

For Africa and the Middle East, the UNESCO World Heritage List includes the following:

Cultural Heritage

- *Abomey, Benin: royal palaces
- Abu Simbel to Philae, Egypt: Nubian monuments
- Accra and Volta, Ghana: forts and castles

- Algiers, Algeria: casbah
- Baalbek, Lebanon
- *Bahia, Oman: fort
- Baku, Azerbaijan: walled city
- Cairo, Egypt: Egyptian Museum
- Carthage, Tunisia: archaeological site
- Damascus, Syria: ancient city
- Fèz, Morocco: medina
- Frankincense Trail, Oman
- Great Zimbabwe National Monument, Zimbabwe
- Halab, Syria: ancient city of Aleppo
- Ile de Gorée, Senegal
- Isfahan, Iran: Meidam Emam
- *Jerusalem, Israel: old city and walls
- Khami Ruins National Monument, Zimbabwe
- Lalibela, Ethiopia: rock-hewn churches
- Marrakesh, Morocco: medina
- Meknès, Morocco: historic city
- Memphis, Egypt: pyramid fields from Giza to Dashur
- Persepolis, Iran: ancient city
- Petra, Jordan
- Robben Island, South Africa
- San'a, Yemen: old city
- Sterkfontein and environs, South Africa: fossil hominid sites
- Sukar, Nigeria: cultural landscape
- Tadrart Acacus, Libya: rock art sites
- Thebes, Egypt: ancient city and necropolis
- *Timbuktu, Mali
- uKhahlamba-Drakensberg Park, South Africa
- Zanzibar, Tanzania: stone town

Natural Heritage

- *Air and Ténéré Natural Reserves, Niger
- Arabian Oryx Sanctuary, Oman
- Banc d'Arguin National Park, Mauritania
- Bandiagara cliffs, Land of the Dogun, Mali
- Bwindi Impenetrable Forest, Uganda
- *Djoudj National Bird Sanctuary, Senegal
- Gough Island Wildlife Reserve, South Atlantic Ocean, west of African continent

- Greater St. Lucia Wetland Park, South Africa
- Groupe d'Aldabra, Seychelles
- Ichkeul National Park, Tunisia
- Kilimanjaro National Park, Tanzania
- Lake Malawi National Park, Malawi
- Mana Pools National Park and Sapi and Chewore safari areas, Zimbabwe
- Mount Kenya National Park and forest, Kenya
- *Mount Nimba Nature Reserve, Guinea/Côte d'Ivorie
- Ngorongoro Conservation Area, Tanzania
- *Parc National de la Garamba, Congo-Kinshasa
- Parc National de la Komoé, Côte d'Ivorie
- *Parc National de la Salonga, Congo-Kinshasa
- *Parc National de Manova-Gounda-St. Floris, Central African Republic
- Parc National de Tai, Côte d'Ivorie
- *Parc National des Virunga, Congo-Kinshasa
- *Parc National du Kahuzi-Biega, Congo-Kinshasa
- Parc National du Niololo Koba, Senegal
- Parc National du "W," Niger
- Réserve du Dja, Cameroon
- *Réserve du Okapi, Congo-Kinshasa
- Réserve du Tsingy Bemaraha, Madagascar
- *Ruwenzori Mountains National Park, Uganda
- Selous Game Reserve, Tanzania
- Serengeti National Park, Tanzania
- Sibiloe and Central Island National Parks, Kenya
- *Simien National Park, Ethiopia
- Tassili n'Ajjer, Algeria
- uKhahlamba-Drakensberg Park, South Africa
- Vallée de Mai Nature Reserve, Seychelles
- Victoria Falls, Zambia/Zimbabwe

■ Reading Suggestions: Africa and the Middle East

- Bartle Bull: *Café on the Nile* (1998) offers romance and adventure in East Africa.
- Sir Richard Francis Burton: This English explorer wrote travel books, including *First Footsteps in Eastern Africa* (1856), an account of his discovery of Lake Tanganyika.

- James Chavell: *Whirlwind* (1986) is a novel set against the 1979 revolution in Iran.

- Agatha Christie: She wrote *Murder on the Orient Express* (1934), which was filmed several times.

- Isak Dinesen (Karen Blixen): *Out of Africa* (1937) begins, "I had a farm in Africa, at the foot of the Ngong Hills"; the renowned work was also filmed.

- Sean Fraser: *African Adventure Atlas* (2004) is a *National Geographic* wish book of route maps that suggest adventure activities in Africa.

- Nadine Gordimer: She is a South African novelist, short story writer, and winner of the Nobel Prize for literature in 1991.

- Ernest Hemingway: *The Short, Happy Life of Francis Macomber* (1938) is a short story of an American couple on safari in Africa.

- James Michener: *The Covenant* (1980) provides a history of South Africa.

- Elizabeth Peters: *The Snake, the Crocodile, and the Dog* (1992) and *Night Train to Memphis* (1994) are detective stories set amidst Egyptian ruins.

- Robert Ruark: *Something of Value* (1955) is an out-of-print novel (available through libraries) of Kenya, safaris, and the Mau Mau uprisings.

- Alexander McCall Smith: *The No. 1 Ladies Detective Agency* (1996) is a best-selling series with descriptions of Botswana's landscape, people, and lifestyles.

- Paul Theroux: *Dark Star Safari* (2003) describes an overland journey from Cairo to Cape Town.

- Leon Uris: *Exodus* (1958) is a classic best-seller about the birth of Israel.

Worksheet 13.1: Geography

Name _____ Date _____

Directions: Answer the questions in the space provided.

1. Which country—home to 125 tribal groups, Ngorongoro Crater, Mount Kilimanjaro, Olduvai Gorge, and Serengeti National Park—is the largest in East Africa?

   _____

2. Africa is linked to the Middle East by the _____ Peninsula.

3. The _____ Gulf separates the Arabian Peninsula from Iran.

4. Describe the Sahel. Why is the region shrinking?

   _____

   _____

   _____

5. Africa's tallest mountain is _____ .

6. Africa's tallest mountains rise near the equator. Given their location, how do you explain the fact that the mountains have glaciers and are snow-covered much of the year?

   _____

   _____

7. The river system that begins in the mountains of Turkey and flows south through Syria and Iraq is the

   _____ .

8. Describe the climate of South Africa.

   _____

   _____

9. Africa has the world's largest desert and the world's longest river. What are they?

   _____

10. When would be the most ideal time to take a safari? Why?

    _____

    _____

11. Which African country produces the most gold?

   _____

12. Africa's largest lake is _____ .

13. Where is the Barbary Coast?

   _____

14. The country that lies completely within South Africa is _____ .

Worksheet 13.2: Itinerary Planning

Name   Date

A trip to Egypt is usually a once-in-a-lifetime event. How would you plan a 2-week vacation for Mr. and Mrs. Steven Jones? They have traveled extensively throughout the United States and Europe but have never ventured to an exotic destination. What do they need to know? What attractions are must-sees? When should they go?

Worksheet 13.3: Answering Questions

Name _____ Date _____

Directions: How would you respond to travelers who asked the following questions?

1. "Are there any cruise itineraries that include ports along the North African coast of the Mediterranean as well as European ports?"

2. "I'm not very good at bargaining, and I understand that to buy anything in Morocco, I must at least attempt to haggle. What should I do?"

Worksheet 13.4: Map Review

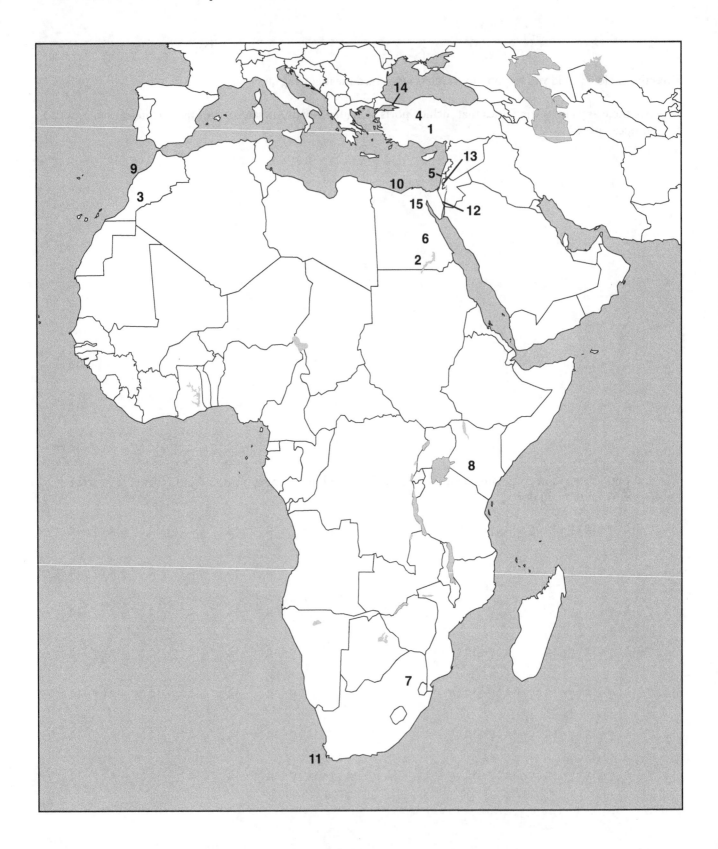

Worksheet 13.4: Map Review

Name _____   Date

Directions: Match the destination with its number on the map. Optional: Use industry or online resources to find the airport code of the destination or the nearest airport.

Map Number   **Airport Code**

_____   Abu Simbel   _____

_____   Alexandria   _____

_____   Ankara   _____

_____   Cairo   _____

_____   Cape Town   _____

_____   Cappadocia   _____

_____   Casablanca   _____

_____   Eilat   _____

_____   Istanbul   _____

_____   Jerusalem   _____

_____   Johannesburg   _____

_____   Luxor   _____

_____   Marrakesh   _____

_____   Nairobi   _____

_____   Tel Aviv   _____

Bonus Question: If you find yourself at zero degrees latitude and zero degrees longitude, where are you?

_____

Worksheet 13.5: Using Reference Materials

Name _____ Date _____

Directions: Using available resources, answer the questions in the space provided. Indicate in your answer what resources you used.

1. Does the U.S. State Department have any advisories about travel to African countries? If so, which ones?

2. What documentation does a U.S. traveler need to visit Tanzania?

3. Does Tanzania have any health problems travelers should be aware of?

4. What is the weather like in Tanzania in March?

Worksheet 13.6: Looking Back: A Chapter Quiz

Name _____ Date _____

Directions: Answer the questions in the space provided, or circle the correct answer.

1. Where are Egypt's most famous pyramids located?

   _____

2. Which African country owes some of its popularity to a series of best-selling detective novels set in this politically stable and geographically unique destination?

   _____

3. How many religions have holy sites in Jerusalem? Name these religions.

   _____

   _____

   _____

   _____

4. Match these Moroccan place-names with their descriptions.

   _____ Casablanca

   _____ Rabat

   _____ Meknes

   _____ Fez

   _____ Marrakesh

   _____ Tangier

   A. Site of a great square and the place to see snake charmers, visit fortune-tellers, and buy some false teeth

   B. Capital (and second largest city of Morocco)

   C. Largest city and the country's international gateway

   D. City on the north coast across from Spain that receives many day-trippers

   E. Site of the great medina and Bâb el-Mansour

   F. Site of the Karaouine Mosque and one of Islam's oldest universities

5. Match these Egyptian place-names with their descriptions.

   _____ Aswan

   _____ Luxor

   _____ Abu Simbel

   _____ Cairo

   A. Temple that was raised to higher ground to save it from the rising waters of the Nile during the construction of the Aswan high dam

   B. Africa's largest city

   C. Location across the Nile from the Valley of the Kings

   D. Popular winter resort

6. **Directions:** Indicate whether each statement is True or False.

True	False	Kalahari is the world's largest desert.
True	False	Thirty to forty people is a good number for an enjoyable safari.
True	False	The pyramids at Giza are one of the Seven Wonders of the ancient world.
True	False	The Muslim workweek is from sunrise on Saturday through sunset on Thursday.
True	False	Light clothing is all that is needed for any trip to Egypt.
True	False	Ben Gurion International Airport in Tel Aviv is Israel's principal international airport.
True	False	Visitors are welcome in the mosques of Turkey, although they may not enter certain areas.
True	False	Cappadocia is a vast volcanic plateau distinguished by its many strange rock formations.

Asia

 Resources

Bangladesh
www.parjatan.org

Bhutan
www.tourism.gov.bt

China
www.cnto.org

Hong Kong
www.discoverhongkong.com

India
www.incredibleindia.org

Indian Rail
www.indianrail.gov.in

Taj hotels
www.tajhotels.com

Indonesia
www.indonesia.travel

Japan
www.jnto.go.jp/eng/

Ryokan Association
www.ryokan.or.jp/english

Korea
www.english.visitkorea.or/kr

Laos
www.tourismlaos.org

Malaysia
www.tourismgov.my

Mongolia
www.visitmongolia.com

Myanmar
www.myanmar-tourism.com

Nepal
www.welcomenepal.com

Philippines
www.itsmorefuninthephilippines
　.com

Singapore
www.yoursingapore.com

Taiwan, Republic of China
www.welcome2taiwan.net

Thailand
www.tourismthailand.org

Bangkok
www.bangkok.com

Vietnam
www.vn-tourism.com

▪ UNESCO World Heritage Sites

For Asia, the UNESCO World Heritage List includes the following:

Cultural Heritage

- Agra Fort, India
- Agra, India: Taj Mahal
- Ajanta Caves, India
- Anaradhapura, Sri Lanka: sacred city
- *Angkor, Cambodia
- Ayutthaya and its region, Thailand: historic towns
- Beijing, China: imperial tombs, palaces, Forbidden City, and Summer Palace
- Borobudur, Java, Indonesia: temple compound
- Dambulla Golden Rock Temple, Sri Lanka
- Darjeeling Himalayan railway, India
- Elephanta Caves, India
- Ellora Temple Caves, India
- Gansu, China: Mogau Caves
- Goa, India: churches and monuments
- Great Wall of China
- Hiroshima, Japan: peace memorial
- Hoe An, Vietnam: ancient town
- Hue, Vietnam: monument complex
- Itsukushima Shrine, Japan
- Kandy, Sri Lanka: Temple of the Sacred Tooth
- Kathmandu Valley, Nepal
- Kyongju, Republic of Korea: historic areas
- Kyoto, Japan: ancient city
- *Lahore, Pakistan: fort and Shalimar gardens
- Lhasa, Tibet, China: Potala Palace and Jokhang Temple Monastery
- Luang Prabang, Laos
- Lumbini, Nepal: birthplace of the Lord Buddha
- Nikko, Japan: shrines and temples
- Prambanan, Java, Indonesia: temple compound
- Qufu, Shandong, China: temple and cemetery of Confucius
- Sangiran, Indonesia: early human site
- Seoul, Republic of Korea: palace complex

- Shirakawa-go and Gokayama, Japan: historic villages
- Sokkuram Grotto and Pulguksa Temple, Republic of Korea
- Sukhothai and its region, Thailand: historic towns
- Xi'an area, China: Terracotta Warriors
- Zhoukoudian, China: archaeological site (Peking Man)

Natural Heritage

- Dambulla Golden Rock Temple, Sri Lanka
- Emei Shan and Leshan Giant Buddha, Sichuan, China
- Gunung Mulu National Park, Malaysia
- Ha Long Bay, Vietnam
- Huang Shan, Anhui, China
- Huanglong scenic and historic interest area, Sichuan, China
- Jiuzhaigou Valley scenic and historic interest area, Sichuan, China
- Kaziranga National Park, India
- Keoladeo National Park, India
- Komodo National Park, Indonesia
- Lorentz National Park, Indonesia
- *Manas Wildlife Sanctuary, India
- Nanda Devi National Park, India
- Puerto-Princesa Subterranean River, Philippines
- Royal Chitwan National Park, Nepal
- Sagarmatha National Park, Nepal
- Shirakami-Sanchi, Japan
- Sinharaja Forest Reserve, Sri Lanka
- Sukhothai and its region and historic towns, Thailand
- Sundarbans, Bangladesh
- Sundarbans National Park, India
- Tai Shan, Shandong, China
- Thung Yai-Huai Kha Khaeng Wildlife Sanctuaries, Thailand
- Tubbataha Reef Marine Park, Philippines
- Ujung Kulon National Park and Krakatau Nature Reserve, Indonesia
- Wulingyuan scenic and historic interest area, Hunan, China
- Wuyl Shan, Fujian, China
- Yaku-shima, Japan

■ Reading Suggestions: Asia

- Pearl Buck: *Imperial Woman* (1956). Another view of the empress. Buck, raised in China, won the Pulitzer Prize in 1932 for *The Good Earth* and the Nobel Prize for literature in 1938.

- Bartle Bull: *Shanghai Station* (2004) is set in 1917 at the start of Chiang Kai-shek's and Mao Tse-tung's fight for the mastery of China.

- James Clavell: *Shogun* (1975) is about Japan in the 1600s. *Tai-Pan* (1966) and *Noble House* (1981), both set in Hong Kong.

- Bruce Feiler: *Learning to Bow* (1991) is a funny book about the culture clash between the United States and Japan.

- Edward M. Forster: *A Passage to India* (1924) is a novel about the British rule in India.

- Graham Greene: *The Quiet American* (1955) is a novel set in Vietnam during the French colonial period.

- Romesh Gunesekera: *Heaven's Edge* (2003) is a novel set in Sri Lanka.

- E. M. Kaye: *Far Pavilions* (1978) is sometimes called India's *Gone with the Wind*.

- Rudyard Kipling: *The Man Who Would Be King* (1889) is set in India, and *Barrack-Room Ballads* (1891) is a collection of poems.

- Margaret Landon: *Anna and the King of Siam* (1903), about a governess who goes to Siam, was made into a Broadway musical and at least three films.

- Anchee Min: *Empress Orchid* (2004) is a novel about the last empress of China, who ruled for 46 years during the decline of the kingdom.

- Paul Scott: *The Raj Quartet* (1966–1975), an epic story of life in India during British rule, was made into Masterpiece Theater's series *The Jewel in the Crown*.

- Stanley Stewart: *In the Empire of Genghis Khan* (2002) is the author's experiences in a destination where few Westerners have ventured.

- Kent R. Weeks: *The Lost Tomb* (1998) is about an American Egyptologist who discovers the burial site of the sons of Ramesses II in 1995.

- Simon Winchester: He wrote *Krakatoa: The Day the World Exploded* (2003).

Worksheet 14.1: Geography

Name _____   Date _____

Directions: Answer the questions in the space provided.

1. How would you describe the climate of India?

   _____

2. What are monsoons?

   _____

   _____

3. When would be the best time of year to visit Tokyo?

   _____

4. Which city was the capital of Japan for more than 1,000 years?

   _____

5. What is meant by the Ring of Fire?

   _____

   _____

6. What is the name of the famous temple complex in Cambodia and the name of the gateway to this site?

   _____

7. What countries are located on the long peninsula of Southeast Asia known as Indochina?

   _____

   _____

   _____

8. What mountain range forms the northern border of India?

   _____

9. What are China's two most important rivers?

   _____

10. Thailand's major river is the _____ .

11. How many time zones does China have?

_____

12. Why does Bangladesh flood so often?

_____

_____

13. Which Asian country is in danger of disappearing if the ocean rises?

_____

14. What four islands make up Japan?

_____

_____

15. What do the suffixes -*pur* and -*abad* mean?

_____

16. Which South Asian country was never a European colony?

_____

17. The world's highest peak, Mount Everest, is located in what Asian kingdom?

_____

Worksheet 14.2: Itinerary Planning

Name   Date

Outline a 2-week vacation for a couple to Thailand. Their interests include history, shopping, and outdoor activities.

Worksheet 14.3: Answering Questions

Name _____ Date _____

Directions: How would you respond to travelers who asked the following questions?

1. What attracts most travelers to Bhutan?

2. "I won't be able to read the menus in Japan. What will I do?"

Worksheet 14.4: Map Review: India and Southeast Asia

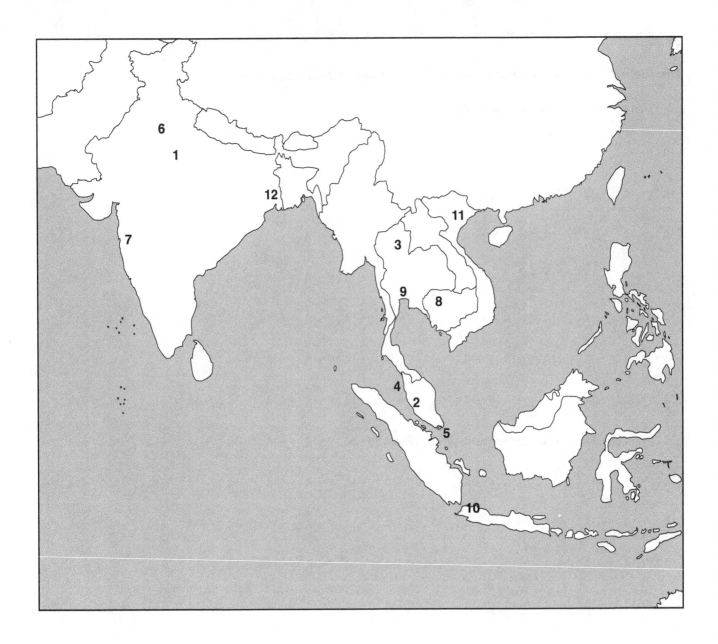

Worksheet 14.4: Map Review: India and Southeast Asia

Name _____ Date

Directions: Match the destination below with the corresponding number on the map. Optional: Use industry or online resources to find the airport code of the destination or the nearest airport.

Map Number   **Airport Code**

_____   Agra   _____

_____   Bangkok   _____

_____   Chiang Mai   _____

_____   Delhi   _____

_____   Hanoi   _____

_____   Jakarta   _____

_____   Kolkata   _____

_____   Kuala Lumpur   _____

_____   Mumbai   _____

_____   Penang   _____

_____   Siem Reap   _____

_____   Singapore   _____

Bonus Question: What famous mountain peak is located in Nepal?

_____

Worksheet 14.5: Map Review: East Asia

Worksheet 14.5: Map Review: East Asia

Name _____   Date _____

Directions: Match the destination below with the corresponding number on the map. Optional: Use industry or online resources to find the airport code of the destination or the nearest airport.

Map Number	Destination	Airport Code
_____	Ch'ang (Yangtze) River Gorge	_____
_____	Forbidden City	_____
_____	Great Wall	_____
_____	Ming Tombs	_____
_____	Potala Palace	_____
_____	Shanghai	_____
_____	Stone Forest	_____
_____	Terracotta Warriors	_____

Bonus Questions

1. Name the two sections of Hong Kong.

   _____

   _____

2. Which is farther south: Tokyo or Taiwan?

   _____

Worksheet 14.6: Using Reference Materials

Name _____   Date _____

Directions: Using available resources, design a 2-week trip to China for a couple. Be sure to include plans for transportation to and around China, accommodations, and sightseeing. Indicate what resources you used.

Keep in mind:

- Market. Who are you designing the trip for?

- Budget. Is it practical?

- International dateline (IDL). Would you route the travelers east or west?

- Time. How long are the international flights?

- Documentation. What is needed for the areas you pick?

- Health. What does the CDC recommend?

- Safety. Are there any U.S. State Department advisories?

- Price. Can you come up with an approximate figure? Would it suit the budget of your couple?

Worksheet 14.7: A Chapter Quiz

Name _____ Date _____

Directions: Answer the questions in the space provided.

1. What is in the Taj Mahal? Where is the Taj Mahal located?

_____

_____

_____

_____

2. What is "Bollywood"?

_____

_____

_____

_____

3. Which Southeast Asian country has one of the absolute monarchies and is one of the world's richest?

_____

_____

_____

_____

4. What is done as a sign of respect before entering a temple, mosque, or private home?

_____

5. **Directions:** Match each architectural work with its location.

_____	Petronas Towers	A. Java
_____	Rock-carved temples	B. Kuala Lumpur
_____	Snake Temple	C. Ajanta
_____	Borobudur	D. Bangkok
_____	Temple of the Emerald Buddha	E. Agra
_____	Taj Mahal	F. Penang

Worksheet 14.8: Looking Back at East Asia: A Chapter Quiz

Name _____ Date _____

Directions: Circle the correct answer, or answer the questions in the space provided.

1. Indicate whether each statement is True or False.

   True   False   Mount Fuji is visible from Tokyo every day of the year.

   True   False   Honshu is the largest Japanese island.

   True   False   Tokyo is a sparsely populated city.

   True   False   The Ginza is an area of Tokyo known for its business district and expensive stores.

   True   False   The Shinkansen is also known as the "Bullet Train."

   True   False   In Japan, people drive on the right.

   True   False   China is the world's largest country.

   True   False   The best time to visit Beijing is spring or fall.

   True   False   After Beijing, Xi'an is China's most popular tourist destination.

   True   False   The 4-hour boat trip on the Li River near Guilin is an exceptional travel experience.

   True   False   In China, people drive on the left.

2. What destination is out of place in the itinerary Tokyo–Hakone–Nikko–Kyoto–Osaka–Taipei?

   _____

3. Which destination is out of place in the itinerary Beijing–Guangzhou–Guilin–Odense–Shanghai–Xi'an?

   _____

4. Which Chinese city is home to a maglev train?

   _____

5. How did Taiwan become independent of China?

   _____

   _____

   _____

   _____

6. What country is Tibet part of? Is Tibet open to tourists?

   _____

   _____

   _____

7. What is the world's most commonly spoken language?

_____

8. Why has the completion date of China's Three Gorges Dam been important to tourism?

_____

_____

9. What is the Forbidden City?

_____

_____

10. What transition took place within Hong Kong in 1997?

_____

_____

11. Why are North and South Korea separate countries?

_____

_____

_____

_____

12. Name two World Heritage attractions on the Indonesian island of Java.

_____

_____

The Pacific

■ Resources

The tourist boards of both Australia and New Zealand promote their countries actively and provide many educational aids. The Pacific Asia Travel Association (PATA) provides information about Australia, New Zealand, and Oceania. Of the travel guides, the *Lonely Planet* series has its headquarters in Melbourne, Australia, so it is no wonder that writing about its own backyard is a specialty. The company publishes more than a dozen titles about the country down under.

As distant and diverse from one another as they are, fourteen islands of the South Pacific are represented by the South Pacific Tourism Organization (SPTO). The islands are Cook Islands, Fiji, Kiribati, Marshall Islands, Nauru, New Caledonia, Niue, Papua New Guinea, Samoa, Solomon Islands, Tahiti, Tonga, Tuvalu, and Vanuatu. You can link to information on each island or island group from SPTO's Web site.

Australia
www.australia.com

Rail Australia
www.railaustralia.com.au

Visa Information
www.immi.gov.au

Capital Territory
www.canberratourism.com.au

New South Wales
www.visitnsw.com

Bridgeclimb
www.bridgeclimb.com

Sydney Opera House
www.sydneyoperahouse.com

Northern Territory
www.travelnt.com.com

Frontier Camel Farm
www.cameltours.com.au

Kakadu Park
www.parksaustralia.gov.au/kakadu

North Queensland
www.ttnq.org.au

Queensland
www.destinationqueensland.com

Brisbane Tourism
www.visitbrisbane.com.au

Gold Coast Tourism
www.visitgoldcoastcom

Great Barrier Reef
www.gbrmpa.gov.au

South Australia
www.southaustralia.com

Tasmania
www.tourism.tasmania.com

Port Arthur
www.portarthur.org.au

Victoria
www.visitvictoria.com

Western Australia
www.westernaustralia.com

New Zealand
www.newzealand.com

Automobile Association
www.nzaa.co.nz

New Zealand Rail
www.transzrail.co.nz

South Pacific Islands
www.spto.org

■ UNESCO World Heritage Sites

For the Pacific, the UNESCO World Heritage List includes the following:

Cultural Heritage

- Kakadu National Park, Australia
- Tasmanian wilderness, Australia
- Uluru-Kata Tjuta National Park, Australia
- Willandra Lakes region, Australia

Natural Heritage

- Central and eastern rain forest reserves, Australia
- East Rennell, Solomon Islands
- Fiordland, Aoraki/Mount Cook and Westland National Parks, New Zealand
- Fraser Island, Australia
- Great Barrier Reef, Australia
- Greater Blue Mountains area, Australia
- Henderson Island, Pitcairn Islands
- Kakadu National Park, Australia
- Lord Howe Island group, Australia
- Naracoorte and Riversleigh mammalian fossil sites, Australia
- Queensland wet tropics, Australia
- Shark Bay, Australia
- Tasmanian wilderness, Australia
- Tongariro National Park, New Zealand
- Uluru-Kata Tjuta National Park, Australia
- Willandra Lakes Region, Australia

Reading Suggestions: The Pacific

- Tony Horwitz: *Blue Latitudes* (2002) is part Cook biography, part travelogue.

- Robert Hughes: *The Fatal Shore*, (1986) a story of Australia, was made into a 9-hour series in 2000 for PBS titled *Beyond the Fatal Shore*.

- Keri Hulme: *The Bone People* is a novel about Maori characters; the author is part Maori.

- William Stuart Long: *The Australians* (1979–1987), which contains ten volumes, is an easy-to-read series of novels about the continent's settlement.

- Dame Ngaio Marsh: This New Zealander wrote detective stories.

- W. Somerset Maugham: *The Moon and the Sixpence* (1919) is based on the life of the artist Paul Gauguin.

- Colleen McCullough: *The Thorn Birds* (1977) is a story of an Outback station. McCullough is also author of *Morgan's Run* (2000), a saga about the first white settlers.

- Margaret Mead: *Coming of Age in Samoa* (1928) is a classic text in social anthropology, a study of adolescent girls in a noncompetitive culture.

- James A. Michener: He wrote *Tales of the South Pacific* (1947) and *Return to Paradise* (1951).

- George Plimpton: He edited *As Told at the Explorer's Club* (2003), fifty tales of adventure from Tahiti to Tibet and all compass points in between, from Explorer's Club members.

- Nevil Shute: *A Town Like Alice* (1950) and *On the Beach* (1957) are two novels set in Australia.

- Paul Theroux: *The Happy Isles of Oceania: Paddling the Pacific* (1992) is a nonfiction work on the problems of paradise.

Worksheet 15.1: Geography

Name _____ Date _____

Directions: Answer the questions in the space provided, or circle the correct answer.

1. What is Oceania?

   _____

   _____

2. Australia's hottest month, and the middle of its summer, is
   A. January.
   B. April.
   C. July.
   D. October.

3. In land area, Australia is almost the size of
   A. France.
   B. China.
   C. Peru.
   D. United States.

4. The Great Dividing Range runs down Australia's _____ coast.
   A. east
   B. west
   C. north
   D. south

5. What is a coral reef?

   _____

   _____

6. The Great Barrier Reef is off the Australian coast of
   A. New South Wales.
   B. Queensland.
   C. Victoria.
   D. South Australia.

7. Travelers seeking Australia's highest mountain should explore the Snowy Mountains in New South Wales and seek out
   A. Mount Kaputar.
   B. Mount Elliot.
   C. Mount Kosciuszko.
   D. Mount Cook.

8. Flowing mostly in South Australia, which river is the country's longest permanently flowing inland waterway?
   A. Avon
   B. Torrens
   C. Murray
   D. Swan

9. New Zealand is separated from Australia by the
   A. Arafura Sea.
   B. Milford Sound.
   C. Tasman Sea.
   D. Indian Ocean.

10. New Zealand's highest mountains are the
    A. Remarkables.
    B. Franz Josefs.
    C. Catlins.
    D. Southern Alps.

11. Bird-watchers seek New Zealand's elusive
    A. kakapo.
    B. emu.
    C. kiwi.
    D. bat.

12. Which of the following is on New Zealand's North Island?
    A. Christchurch
    B. Wellington
    C. Tasman Glacier
    D. Dunedin

13. Where are the Waitomo Caves, and what do people go there to see?

    _____

    _____

14. What is Melanesia?

    _____

    _____

    _____

15. What is an atoll?

    _____

    _____

16. Fiji's international gateway is _____ on the island of Viti Levu.
    A. Nandi
    B. Suva
    C. Nausori
    D. Lautoka

Worksheet 15.1: Geography (continued)

Name _____   Date _____

17. Papua New Guinea is on the _____ half of the island of New Guinea.
    A. northern
    B. southern
    C. eastern
    D. western

18. Travelers can cruise Papua New Guinea's _____ River on voyages of exploration to the island's interior.
    A. Fly
    B. Ramu
    C. Sepik
    D. Strickland

19. Name three French Polynesian islands that attract travelers.

    _____

    _____

20. Heart-shaped _____ is the South Sea isle of the travel brochures.
    A. Tetiaroa
    B. Tutuila
    C. Moorea
    D. Aitutaki

21. _____ is an island near Japan with a large U.S. naval base.
    A. Tonga
    B. Fiji
    C. Guam
    D. Tahiti

Worksheet 15.2: Itinerary Planning

Name _____ Date _____

The travelers have only a 2-week vacation and want to visit the Pacific region. They are very active and enjoy hiking and physically challenging activities. What would you suggest for them?

Worksheet 15.3: Answering Questions

_____

Name   Date

Directions: How would you respond to travelers who asked the following questions?

1. "Isn't a trip to Australia very expensive?"

2. "Isn't New Zealand just a lot of scenery and outdoor activities?"

3. "Can I see the places in New Zealand where the *Lord of the Rings* trilogy was filmed?"

Worksheet 15.4: Map Review

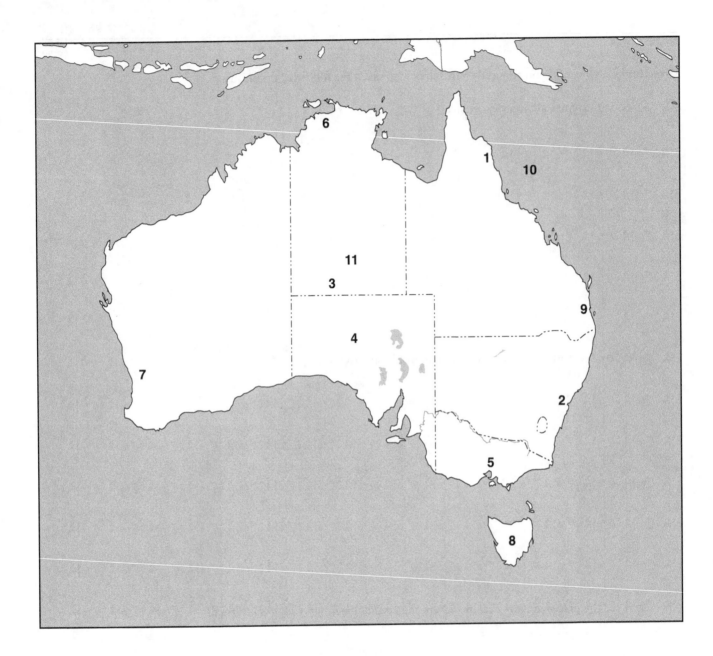

Worksheet 15.4: Map Review

Name _____

Date _____

Directions: Match the destination listed with its corresponding letter on the map. Optional: Use industry or online resources to find the airport code of the destination or the nearest airport.

Map Number   **Airport Code**

_____   Alice Springs   _____

_____   Brisbane   _____

_____   Cairns   _____

_____   Coober Pedy   _____

_____   Darwin   _____

_____   Great Barrier Reef _____

_____   Hobart   _____

_____   Melbourne   _____

_____   Perth   _____

_____   Sydney   _____

_____   Uluru (Ayers Rock) _____

Bonus Question: Name the highest mountain in Papua New Guinea.

_____

Worksheet 15.5: Using Reference Materials

Name _____   Date _____

Directions: Using available resources, answer the questions in the space provided. Indicate in your answer what resource you used.

1. From your city, how would you route travelers who want to fly to Australia and New Zealand?

2. What documentation do they need to visit Australia? New Zealand?

3. What type of hotel accommodations are available in Alice Springs?

4. Are there any special events in either Australia or New Zealand that you think the travelers would enjoy?

Worksheet 15.6: Looking Back: A Chapter Quiz

Name _____ Date

Directions: Circle the correct answer, or write the answer in the space provided.

1. Ayers Rock is closest to the Outback town of
   A. Coober Pedy.
   B. Alice Springs.
   C. Broken Hill.
   D. Broome.

2. The Indian Pacific Railway offers a train ride across the Nullabor Plain between
   A. Cairns and Darwin.
   B. Brisbane and Alice Springs.
   C. Canberra and Adelaide.
   D. Perth and Sydney.

3. Australia's famous opera house designed by Danish architect Joern Utzum is found in
   A. Canberra.
   B. Brisbane.
   C. Melbourne.
   D. Sydney.

4. This city is a gateway to the Great Barrier Reef.
   A. Cairns
   B. Melbourne
   C. Brisbane
   D. Townsville

5. New Zealand's largest city is
   A. Auckland.
   B. Christchurch.
   C. Wellington.
   D. Invercargill.

6. The world-renowned Milford Sound is found in _____ National Park.
   A. Fiordland
   B. Egmont
   C. Tongariro
   D. Mount Cook

7. New Zealand's capital city is
   A. Auckland.
   B. Christchurch.
   C. Hamilton.
   D. Wellington.

8. _____ is the starting point for the 5-day hike to Milford Sound.
   A. Invercargill
   B. Queenstown
   C. Twizel
   D. Te Anau

9. The Maori equivalent of a luau is called a
   A. *pakha.*
   B. *hangi.*
   C. *meke.*
   D. *kumara.*

10. Match the place-names with the descriptions that follow.

Fiji Guam Tonga Tahiti Papua New Guinea

_____ A. It is composed of a double chain of islands south of the equator and just west of the international date line and is the only remaining kingdom in the Pacific.

_____ B. It is called the "Crossroads of the South Pacific," Viti Levu and Vanua Levu are its two largest islands.

_____ C. Sing-sing Festivals and primitive art are just two of the attractions of this country.

_____ D. This is an island near Japan with a large U.S. naval base.

_____ E. This is one of the Society Islands of French Polynesia and is known for its capital, the city of Papeete.

An Exclusive Career Opportunity

Students who complete a course of study using *Exploring the World* can take the Geography for Travel Professionals Test, and after passing, receive the Geography for Travel Professionals Test Certificate. The test consists of 100 multiple-choice questions.

Visit www.thetravelinstitute.com/testing for more information.

Sample Test Questions

1. If it is 5:00 PM in Los Angeles, California (GMT –8), what time is it in Bermuda (GMT – 4)?
   A. 2:00 PM
   B. 9:00 PM (correct answer)
   C. 2:00 AM
   D. 1:00 PM

2. Which destination is out of place in this list of New England attractions?
   A. Mad River Valley
   B. Freedom Trail
   C. Liberty Bell (correct answer)
   D. The Breakers

3. Accommodations in Spain include the government-run chain of three- to five-star hotels located in castles, former convents, medieval fortresses, and modern properties known as
   A. *pousadas.*
   B. paradores. (correct answer)
   C. pensions.
   D. *albergos.*